HIGHER

2007

[BLANK PAGE]

OFFICIAL SQA PAST PAPERS WITH ANSWERS

HIGHER

BIOLOGY
2007-2011

Publisher's Note

We are delighted to bring you the 2011 Past Papers and you will see that we have changed the format from previous editions. As part of our environmental awareness strategy, we have attempted to make these new editions as sustainable as possible.

To do this, we have printed on white paper and bound the answer sections into the book. This not only allows us to use significantly less paper but we are also, for the first time, able to source all the materials from sustainable sources.

We hope you like the new editions and by purchasing this product, you are not only supporting an independent Scottish publishing company but you are also, in the International Year of Forests, not contributing to the destruction of the world's forests.

Thank you for your support and please see the following websites for more information to support the above statement –

www.fsc-uk.org

www.loveforests.com

© Scottish Qualifications Authority
All rights reserved. Copying prohibited. No part of this publication may be reproduced, stored in a retrieval system, or transmitted in any form or by any means, electronic, mechanical, photocopying, recording or otherwise.

First exam published in 2007.
Published by Bright Red Publishing Ltd, 6 Stafford Street, Edinburgh EH3 7AU
tel: 0131 220 5804 fax: 0131 220 6710 info@brightredpublishing.co.uk www.brightredpublishing.co.uk

ISBN 978-1-84948-209-7

A CIP Catalogue record for this book is available from the British Library.

Bright Red Publishing is grateful to the copyright holders, as credited on the final page of the Question Section, for permission to use their material. Every effort has been made to trace the copyright holders and to obtain their permission for the use of copyright material.
Bright Red Publishing will be happy to receive information allowing us to rectify any error or omission in future editions.

FOR OFFICIAL USE

Total for
Sections
B and C

X007/301

NATIONAL
QUALIFICATIONS
2007

MONDAY, 21 MAY
1.00 PM – 3.30 PM

BIOLOGY
HIGHER

Fill in these boxes and read what is printed below.

Full name of centre

Town

Forename(s)

Surname

Date of birth
Day Month Year   Scottish candidate number   Number of seat

SECTION A–Questions 1—30 (30 marks)

Instructions for completion of Section A are given on page two.

For this section of the examination you must use an **HB pencil.**

SECTIONS B AND C (100 marks)

1 (a) All questions should be attempted.

  (b) It should be noted that in **Section C** questions 1 and 2 each contain a choice.

2 The questions may be answered in any order but all answers are to be written in the spaces provided in this answer book, **and must be written clearly and legibly in ink.**

3 Additional space for answers will be found at the end of the book. If further space is required, supplementary sheets may be obtained from the invigilator and should be inserted inside the **front** cover of this book.

4 The numbers of questions must be clearly inserted with any answers written in the additional space.

5 Rough work, if any should be necessary, should be written in this book and then scored through when the fair copy has been written. If further space is required a supplementary sheet for rough work may be obtained from the invigilator.

6 Before leaving the examination room you must give this book to the invigilator. If you do not, you may lose all the marks for this paper.

SCOTTISH
QUALIFICATIONS
AUTHORITY

Read carefully

1 Check that the answer sheet provided is for **Biology Higher (Section A)**.

2 For this section of the examination you must use an **HB pencil**, and where necessary, an eraser.

3 Check that the answer sheet you have been given has **your name**, **date of birth**, **SCN** (Scottish Candidate Number) and **Centre Name** printed on it.

Do not change any of these details.

4 If any of this information is wrong, tell the Invigilator immediately.

5 If this information is correct, **print** your name and seat number in the boxes provided.

6 The answer to each question is **either** A, B, C or D. Decide what your answer is, then, using your pencil, put a horizontal line in the space provided (see sample question below).

7 There is **only one correct** answer to each question.

8 Any rough working should be done on the question paper or the rough working sheet, **not** on your answer sheet.

9 At the end of the exam, put the **answer sheet for Section A inside the front cover of this answer book**.

Sample Question

The apparatus used to determine the energy stored in a foodstuff is a

A   calorimeter

B   respirometer

C   klinostat

D   gas burette.

The correct answer is **A**—calorimeter. The answer **A** has been clearly marked in **pencil** with a horizontal line (see below).

Changing an answer

If you decide to change your answer, carefully erase your first answer and using your pencil fill in the answer you want. The answer below has been changed to **D**.

SECTION A

All questions in this section should be attempted.

Answers should be given on the separate answer sheet provided.

1. Which line in the table identifies correctly the two cell structures shown in the diagram?

	X	Y
A	Golgi body	Vesicle
B	Golgi body	Ribosome
C	Endoplasmic reticulum	Vesicle
D	Endoplasmic reticulum	Ribosome

2. The phospholipid molecules in a cell membrane allow the

   A free passage of glucose molecules

   B self-recognition of cells

   C active transport of ions

   D membrane to be fluid.

3. Red blood cells have a solute concentration of around 0·9%.

   Which of the following statements correctly describes the fate of these cells when immersed in a 1% salt solution?

   A The cells will burst.

   B The cells will shrink.

   C The cells will expand but not burst.

   D The cells will remain unaffected.

4. Which graph best illustrates the effect of increasing temperature on the rate of active uptake of ions by roots?

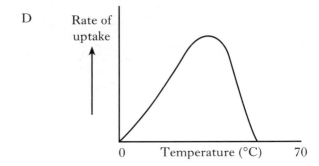

5. Which substances must be provided by host cells for the synthesis of viruses?

A   Proteins and nucleotides

B   Amino acids and DNA

C   Proteins and DNA

D   Amino acids and nucleotides

6. The action spectrum of photosynthesis is a measure of the ability of plants to

A   absorb all wavelengths of light

B   absorb light of different intensities

C   use light to build up foods

D   use light of different wavelengths for synthesis.

7. The diagram shows DNA during replication. Base H represents thymine and base M represents guanine. Which letters represent the base cytosine?

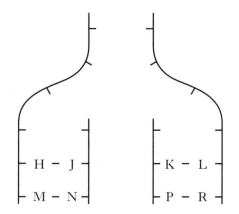

A   J and K

B   J and L

C   N and P

D   N and R

8. The graph below shows the effect of light intensity on the rate of photosynthesis at different temperatures.

Which of the following conclusions can be made from the above data?

A   Only at light intensities greater than 20 units does temperature affect the rate of photosynthesis.

B   At point Y, the rate of photosynthesis is limited by the light intensity.

C   Temperature has little effect on the rate of photosynthesis at low light intensities.

D   At point X, temperature limits the rate of photosynthesis.

9. The cell structures shown below have been magnified ten thousand times.

Mitochondrion

Chloroplast

0·04 micrometres

0·065 micrometres

Expressed as a simple whole number ratio, the length of the mitochondrion compared to that of the chloroplast is

A   8 : 13

B   13 : 8

C   40 : 65

D   65 : 40.

10. A section of a DNA molecule contains 300 bases. Of these bases, 90 are adenine. How many cytosine bases would this section of DNA contain?

   A   60

   B   90

   C   120

   D   180

11. What information can be derived from the recombination frequencies of linked genes?

   A   The mutation rate of the genes

   B   The order and location of genes on a chromosome

   C   Whether genes are recessive or dominant

   D   The genotype for a particular characteristic

12. The diagram shows a family tree for a family with a history of red-green colour deficiency.

 Unaffected male

 Affected male

 Unaffected female

 Affected female

The allele for red-green colour deficiency is sex-linked.

Which of the following statements is true?

   A   Only the son is a carrier.

   B   Only the daughter is a carrier.

   C   Both son and daughter are carriers.

   D   Neither son nor daughter is a carrier.

13. Apple crop yields have been increased by plant breeders selecting for

   A   disease resistance

   B   flavour

   C   resistance to bruising

   D   sugar content.

14. Human insulin can be produced by the bacterium *E. coli* using the following steps.

   1   Culture large quantities of *E. coli* in vats of nutrients.

   2   Insert human insulin gene into *E. coli* plasmid DNA.

   3   Cut insulin gene from human chromosome using enzymes.

   4   Extract insulin from culture vats.

   The correct order for these steps is

   A   3, 2, 1, 4

   B   3, 1, 2, 4

   C   1, 4, 3, 2

   D   1, 2, 3, 4.

15. In a desert mammal, which of the following is a physiological adaptation which helps to conserve water?

   A   Nocturnal foraging

   B   Breathing humid air in a burrow

   C   Having few sweat glands

   D   Remaining underground by day

16. The following factors affect the transpiration rate in a plant.

   1   increasing wind speed

   2   decreasing humidity

   3   rising air pressure

   4   falling temperature

   Which two of these factors would cause an increase in transpiration rate?

   A   1 and 2

   B   1 and 3

   C   2 and 4

   D   3 and 4

[Turn over

17. When first exposed to a harmless stimulus, a group of animals responded by showing avoidance behaviour. When the stimulus was repeated the animals became habituated to it.

What change in response would have shown that habituation was taking place?

A   An increase in the length of the response

B   A decrease in the time taken to respond

C   An increase in response to other stimuli

D   A decrease in the percentage of animals responding

18. In tomato plants, the allele for curled leaves is dominant over the allele for straight leaves. The allele for hairy stems is dominant over the allele for hairless stems. The genes for curliness and hairiness are located on different chromosomes.

If plants heterozygous for both characteristics were crossed, what ratio of phenotypes would be expected in the offspring?

A   All curly and hairy

B   3 curly and hairy: 1 straight and hairless

C   9 curly and hairy: 3 curly and hairless:
    3 straight and hairy: 1 straight and hairless

D   1 curly and hairy: 1 curly and hairless:
    1 straight and hairy: 1 straight and hairless

19. The bar graph below shows changes in the DNA content per cell during stages of meiosis.

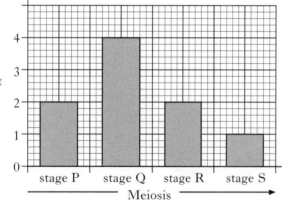

When do the homologous pairs of chromosomes separate?

A   Before the start of stage P

B   Between stages P and Q

C   Between stages Q and R

D   Between stages R and S

20. The genes for two different characteristics are located on separate chromosomes.

In a cross between individuals with the genotypes AaBb and aabb, what is the chance of any one of the offspring having the genotype aabb?

A   0

B   1 in 2

C   1 in 4

D   1 in 8

21. Which line in the table identifies correctly the main source of body heat and the method of controlling body temperature in an endotherm?

	Main source of body heat	Principal method of controlling body temperature
A	Respiration	Behavioural
B	Respiration	Physiological
C	Absorbed from environment	Behavioural
D	Absorbed from environment	Physiological

22. The following four statements relate to meristems.

1   Some provide cells for increase in diameter in stems

2   Some produce growth substances

3   They are found in all growing organisms

4   Their cells undergo division by meiosis

Which of the above statements are true?

A   1 and 2 only

B   1 and 3 only

C   2 and 3 only

D   2 and 4 only

23. The diagram below shows a transverse section of a woody stem.

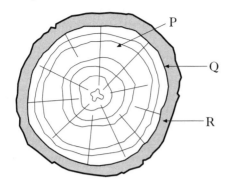

Which line of the table identifies correctly the tissues P, Q and R?

	P	Q	R
A	cambium	xylem	phloem
B	phloem	xylem	cambium
C	xylem	phloem	cambium
D	xylem	cambium	phloem

24. The graph below shows changes which occur in the masses of protein, fat and carbohydrate in a girl's body during seven weeks of starvation.

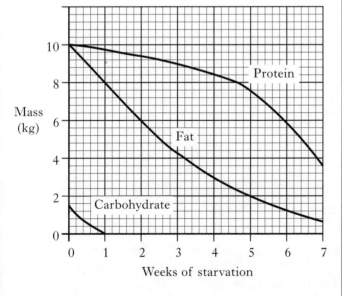

Weeks of starvation

The girl weighs 60 kg at the start. Predict her weight after two weeks without food.

A   43 kg

B   50 kg

C   54 kg

D   57 kg

25. Which of the following is triggered by the hypothalamus in response to an increase in the temperature of the body?

A   Contraction of the hair erector muscles and vasodilation of the skin capillaries

B   Relaxation of the hair erector muscles and vasodilation of the skin capillaries

C   Contraction of the hair erector muscles and vasoconstriction of the skin capillaries

D   Relaxation of the hair erector muscles and vasoconstriction of the skin capillaries

26. Plants require macro-elements for the synthesis of various compounds. Identify which macro-elements are required for synthesis of the compounds shown in the table below.

	Chlorophyll	Protein	ATP
A	phosphorus	magnesium	nitrogen
B	phosphorus	nitrogen	magnesium
C	magnesium	nitrogen	phosphorus
D	magnesium	phosphorus	nitrogen

27. The following are events occurring during germination in barley.

1   The embryo produces gibberellic acid (GA)

2   α-amylase is produced

3   Gibberellic acid (GA) passes to the aleurone layer

4   α-amylase converts starch to maltose

5   Maltose is used by the embryo

Which of the following indicates the correct sequence of events?

A   1 2 4 5 3

B   1 3 2 4 5

C   3 2 1 4 5

D   5 1 3 2 4

[Turn over

28. The table shows the masses of various substances in the glomerular filtrate and in the urine over a period of 24 hours.

Which of the substances has the smallest percentage of reabsorption from the glomerular filtrate?

	Substance	Mass in glomerular filtrate (g)	Mass in urine (g)
A	Sodium	600·0	6·0
B	Potassium	35·0	2·0
C	Uric acid	8·5	0·8
D	Calcium	5·0	0·2

29. An investigation was carried out into the effect of indole acetic acid (IAA) concentration on the shoot growth of two species of plant. The graph below shows a summary of the results.

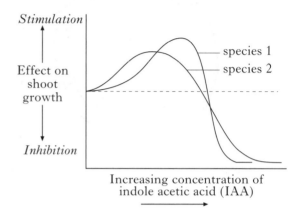

Which one of the following conclusions is justified?

A   Species 1 shows its maximum stimulation at a lower IAA concentration than species 2.

B   Species 2 is more inhibited by the highest concentrations of IAA than species 1.

C   Species 2 is stimulated over a greater range of IAA concentrations than species 1.

D   Species 1 is stimulated by some IAA concentrations which inhibit species 2.

30. An enzyme and its substrate were incubated with various concentrations of either copper or magnesium salts.

The time taken for the complete breakdown of the substrate was measured.

The results are given in the table.

Salt Concentration (M)	Time needed to break down substrate (s)	
	Copper salts	Magnesium salts
0	39	39
1×10^{-8}	42	21
1×10^{-6}	380	49
1×10^{-4}	1480	286

(increasing concentration)

From the data, it may be deduced that

A   high concentrations of copper salts promote the activity of the enzyme

B   high concentrations of copper salts inhibit the activity of the enzyme

C   low concentrations of magnesium salts inhibit the activity of the enzyme

D   high concentrations of magnesium salts promote the activity of the enzyme.

Candidates are reminded that the answer sheet MUST be returned INSIDE the front cover of this answer book.

[Turn over for Section B on *Page ten*

Marks

SECTION B

All questions in this section should be attempted.

All answers must be written clearly and legibly in ink.

1. (*a*) The diagram contains information about light striking a leaf.

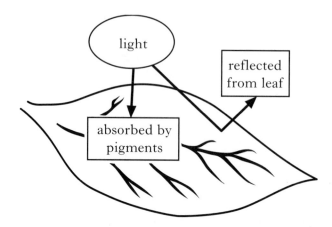

(i) Apart from being absorbed or reflected, what can happen to light which strikes a leaf?

_____   1

(ii) Pigments that absorb light are found within leaf cells.

State the exact location of these pigments.

_____   1

(*b*) The diagram below shows part of the light dependent stage of photosynthesis.

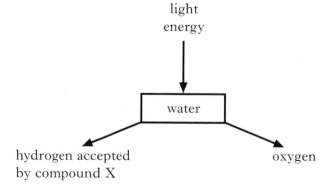

(i) Name this part of the light dependent stage.

_____   1

(ii) Name compound X.

_____   1

Marks

1. **(continued)**

(c) The following sentences describe events in the carbon fixation stage of photosynthesis.

Underline one alternative in each pair to make the sentences correct.

The $\begin{Bmatrix} \text{three} \\ \text{five} \end{Bmatrix}$ carbon compound ribulose bisphosphate (RuBP) accepts

$\begin{Bmatrix} \text{carbon dioxide} \\ \text{hydrogen} \end{Bmatrix}$.

$\begin{Bmatrix} \text{Carbon dioxide} \\ \text{Hydrogen} \end{Bmatrix}$ is accepted by the $\begin{Bmatrix} \text{three} \\ \text{five} \end{Bmatrix}$ carbon compound

glycerate phosphate (GP).

2

[Turn over

Marks

2.   The diagram shows apparatus set up to investigate the rate of respiration in an earthworm. After 10 minutes at 20 °C the level of liquid in the capillary tube had changed as shown.

(a)   (i)   What volume of oxygen is used by the earthworm during the 10 minute period?

_____ cm^3 **1**

(ii)   Describe a suitable control for this experiment.

_____

_____   **1**

(b)   In a second experiment, a worm of 5 grams used 0·5 cm^3 of oxygen in 10 minutes.

Calculate its rate of respiration in cm^3 per minute per gram of worm.

Space for calculation

_____ cm^3 per minute per gram of worm   **1**

[Turn over for Question 3 on *Page fourteen*

Marks

3. (*a*) Samples of carrot tissue were immersed in a hypotonic solution at two different temperatures for 5 hours. The mass of the tissue samples was measured every hour and the percentage change in mass calculated.

The results are shown on the graph.

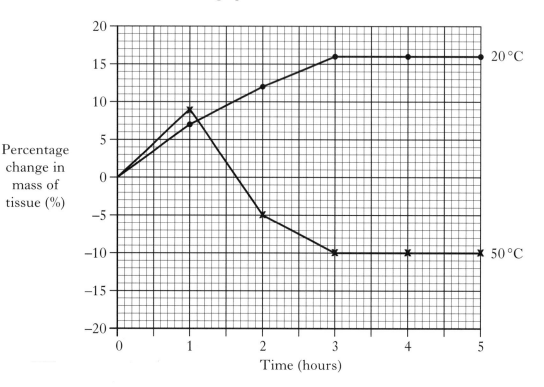

(i) Explain the results obtained at 20 °C from 0 to 3 hours and from 3 hours to 5 hours.

0 to 3 hours _____

_____ 1

3 to 5 hours _____

_____ 1

(ii) Explain the change in mass of the carrot tissue between 1 and 3 hours at 50 °C.

_____

_____

_____ 2

Marks

3.   (continued)

(b)   The chart shows the concentration of ions within a unicellular organism and in the sea water surrounding it.

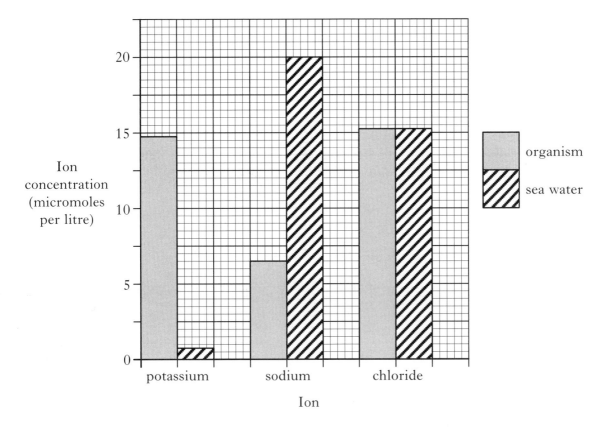

(i)   From the information given, identify the ion which appears to move between the organism and the sea water by diffusion.

Justify your choice.

Ion _____

Justification _____

_____   1

(ii)   When oxygen was bubbled through a tank of sea water containing these organisms, the potassium ion concentration within the organisms increased.

Explain this effect.

_____

_____

_____   2

[Turn over

Marks

4. The diagram shows events occurring during the synthesis of a protein that is secreted from a cell.

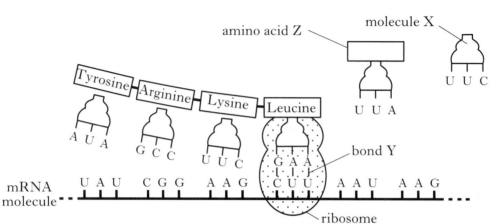

(*a*) (i) Name molecule X. _____   1

  (ii) Name bond Y. _____   1

(*b*) What name is given to a group of three bases on mRNA that codes for an amino acid?

_____   1

(*c*) Give the sequence of DNA bases that codes for amino acid Z.

_____   1

(*d*) Describe the roles of the endoplasmic reticulum and the Golgi apparatus between the synthesis of the protein and its release from the cell.

Endoplasmic reticulum _____

_____   1

Golgi apparatus _____

_____   1

(*e*) The table contains some information about the structure and function of proteins.

Add information to the boxes to complete the table.

Protein	Structure (*Globular or Fibrous*)	Function
Cellulase		
Collagen		Structural protein in skin

2

Marks

5. (a) The graph shows the relationship between plant species diversity in grassland and grazing intensity by herbivores.

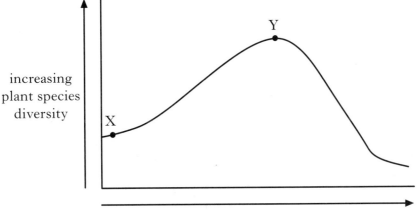

increasing plant species diversity

increasing grazing intensity by herbivores

   (i) Explain the effect on plant species diversity of increased grazing intensity by herbivores between X and Y on the graph.

_____

_____

_____   2

   (ii) What evidence is there that grassland contains plant species tolerant of grazing?

_____

_____   1

   (b) State **one** feature of some plant species that allows them to tolerate grazing by herbivores.

_____

_____   1

[Turn over

6. Norway Spruce (*Picea abies*) is an evergreen species of tree with needle-like leaves, found in regions with extremely cold winters.

The rate of photosynthesis of the species is at its maximum during spring then decreases from June to December.

In an investigation, a sample of one-year-old seedlings was collected in each month from June to December.

For each sample of seedlings, the following measurements were made and averages calculated.

- Dry mass of whole seedlings
- Dry mass of roots only
- Starch content in needles
- Sugar content in needles

The results are shown in **Graphs 1** and **2**.

Graph 1

Graph 2

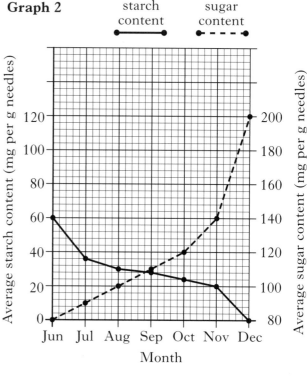

Marks

(a) (i) **Use values from Graph 1** to describe the changes in average dry mass of whole seedlings from June to December.

_____

_____   2

(ii) Between which two months was there the greatest increase in average dry mass of the seedlings' roots only?

Tick (✓) **one** box.

Jun–Jul   Jul–Aug   Aug–Sept   Sept–Oct   Oct–Nov   Nov–Dec

☐   ☐   ☐   ☐   ☐   ☐   1

(iii) **From Graph 2**, calculate the ratio of average starch content to average sugar content in the needles in November.

Space for calculation

_____ Starch: _____ Sugar   1

Marks

6. (*a*) (continued)

(iv) **From Graph 2**, calculate the percentage decrease in average starch content in the needles between June and October.

Space for calculation

_____ % decrease 1

(*b*) Explain the decrease in average starch content in the needles between June and December.

_____

_____ 1

(*c*) Raffinose is a sugar that prevents frost damage to needles.

The table shows the raffinose content of needles from the seedling samples.

Month	*Raffinose content* (mg per g of needles)
June	0
July	1
August	2
September	3
October	9
November	30
December	50

(i) What evidence is there that raffinose is not the only sugar present in the needles of Norway Spruce?

_____

_____ 1

(ii) Suggest how the changing raffinose content of needles from June to December is of survival value to Norway Spruce.

_____

_____ 1

[Turn over

Marks

7. The diagram shows stages in meiosis during which a mutation occurred and the effect of the mutation on the gametes produced.

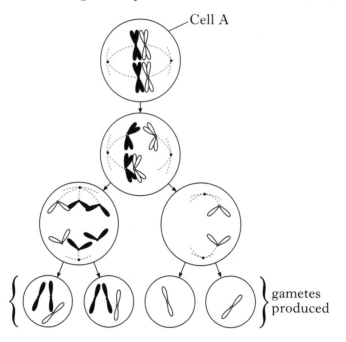

Cell A

gametes
produced

(*a*) (i) What name is given to cells such as cell A, that undergo meiosis?

_____ 1

(ii) Cell A contains two pairs of homologous chromosomes.

Apart from size and shape, state **one** similarity between homologous chromosomes.

_____ 1

(iii) This mutation has resulted in changes to the chromosome numbers in the gametes.

Name this type of mutation.

_____ 1

(iv) State whether the mutation has occurred in the first or second meiotic division and justify your choice.

Meiotic division _____

Justification _____

_____ 1

(v) State the expected haploid number of chromosomes in the gametes produced if this mutation **had not occurred**.

_____ 1

7.   (continued)   *Marks*

(b)   The diagram represents the sequence of bases on part of one strand of a DNA molecule.

Part of DNA molecule   T   G   A   A   C   T   G

The effects of two different gene mutations on the strand of DNA are shown below.

Gene mutation 1   T   T   G   A   A   C   T   G

Gene mutation 2   T   G   A   C   C   T   G

Complete the table by naming the type of gene mutation that has occurred in each case.

Gene Mutation	Name
1	
2	

2

[Turn over

Marks

8. The table shows information about three species of oak tree that have evolved from a common ancestor.

	Oak Species		
	Sessile Oak	Kermes Oak	Northern Red Oak
Leaf Shape	Rounded lobes	Sharp spines	Lobes with sharp spines
Growing Conditions	Mild and damp	Hot and dry	Cool and dry

(a) (i) The Oak species have evolved in ecological isolation.

State the importance of isolating mechanisms in the evolution of new species.

_____   **1**

(ii) Use the information to explain how the evolution of the Oak species illustrates adaptive radiation.

_____

_____   **2**

(b) The Kermes Oak grows to a maximum height of one metre.

Explain the benefit to this species of having leaves with sharp spines.

_____

_____   **1**

(c) To maintain genetic diversity, species must be conserved.

State **two** ways in which species can be conserved.

1 _____

2 _____   **1**

Marks

9. (*a*) The graph shows the body mass of a human male from birth until 22 years of age.

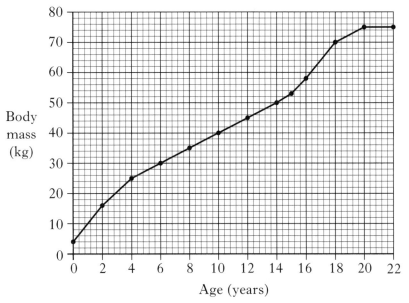

Age (years)

(i) Calculate the average yearly increase in body mass between age 6 and age 14.

Space for calculation

_____ kg **1**

(ii) Explain how the activity of the pituitary gland could account for the growth pattern between 15 and 22 years of age shown on the graph.

_____

_____

_____ **2**

(*b*) The diagram shows the role of the pituitary gland in the secretion of a hormone from the thyroid gland.

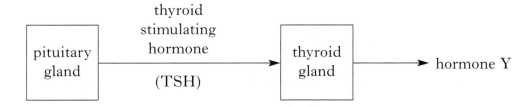

Name hormone Y and describe its role in the control of growth and development.

Hormone Y _____ **1**

Role _____ **1**

Marks

10. An experiment was carried out to investigate the effect of gibberellic acid (GA) on the growth of dwarf pea plants. GA can be absorbed by leaves.

Six identical pea plants were placed in pots containing 100 g of soil. The leaves of each were sprayed with an equal volume of water containing a different mass of GA. The soil in each pot received 20 cm³ water each day and the plants were continuously exposed to equal light intensity from above.

After seven days the stem height of each plant was measured and the percentage increase in stem height calculated.

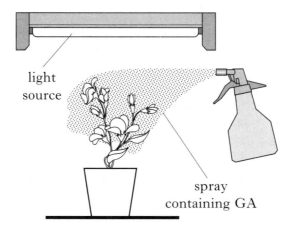

(a) (i) Identify **two** variables, not already mentioned, that should have been controlled to ensure the experimental procedure was valid.

Variable 1 _____   1

Variable 2 _____   1

(ii) State **one** way in which the experimental procedure could be improved to increase the reliability of the results.

_____

_____   1

(b) The results of the experiment are shown in the table.

Mass of GA applied (micrograms)	Percentage increase in stem height (%)
0·01	90
0·03	120
0·05	160
0·08	240
0·10	320
0·11	350

Marks

10. (*b*) (continued)

(i) On the grid provided, complete the line graph to show the percentage increase in stem height against the mass of GA applied.

Use an appropriate scale to fill most of the grid.

(Additional graph paper, if required, will be found on page 36.)

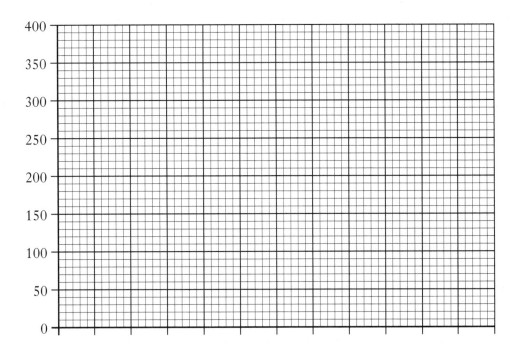

2

(ii) Another pea plant was treated in the same way, using a water spray containing 0·12 micrograms of GA. Predict the percentage increase in stem height of this plant after seven days.

_____ percentage increase   1

(*c*) Explain why the method of application of GA could lead to errors in the results.

_____

_____   1

[Turn over

Marks

11. (*a*) The bacterium *Escherichia coli* can control its lactose metabolism.

Complete **all** boxes in the table to show whether each statement is true (T) or false (F) if lactose is present or absent in the medium in which *E. coli* is growing.

Statement	*Lactose present*	*Lactose absent*
Regulator gene produces the repressor molecule		
Repressor molecule binds to inducer		
Repressor molecule binds to operator		
Structural gene switched on	T	F

2

(*b*) Part of a metabolic pathway involving the amino acid phenylalanine is shown in the diagram.

digestion of
protein in diet $\longrightarrow$ **phenylalanine** $\xrightarrow{\text{enzyme A}}$ **tyrosine** $\xrightarrow{\text{enzyme B}}$ **other compounds**

Phenylketonuria (PKU) is an inherited condition in which enzyme A is either absent or does not function.

(i) Predict the effect on the concentrations of phenylalanine and tyrosine if enzyme A is absent.

Phenylalanine _____   1

Tyrosine _____   1

(ii) PKU is caused by a mutation of the gene that codes for enzyme A.

Explain how a mutation of a gene can cause the production of an altered enzyme.

_____

_____

_____   2

Marks

12. An experiment was set up to investigate the effect of photoperiod on flowering in *Chrysanthemum* plants. Four plants A, B, C and D were exposed to different periods of light and dark in 24 hours. This was repeated every day for several weeks and the effects on flowering noted.

The periods of light and dark and their effects on flowering are shown in the diagram.

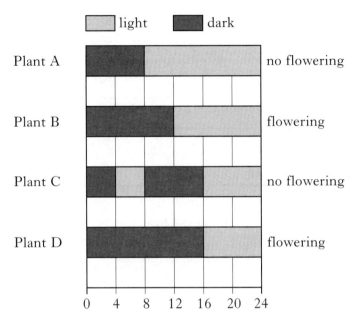

(a) From the information given, identify the conditions required for flowering in *Chrysanthemum* plants. Justify your answer.

Conditions _____

Justification _____

_____ 1

(b) Flowering in response to photoperiod ensures plants within a population flower at the same time. Explain how this enables genetic variation to be maintained.

_____

_____ 1

(c) Mammals also show photoperiodism.

Describe how one type of mammal behaviour can be affected by photoperiod.

_____

_____ 1

[Turn over

Marks

13. The homeostatic control of blood glucose concentration carried out by the human liver is shown on the diagram.

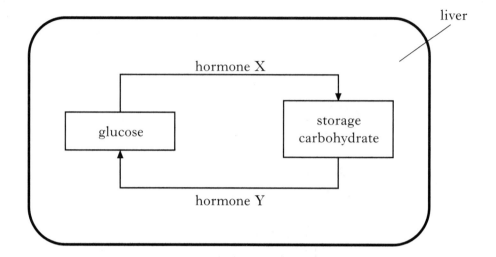

(*a*) Name the storage carbohydrate found in the liver.

_____   1

(*b*) (i) Name hormones X and Y.

Hormone X _____

Hormone Y _____   1

(ii) Name the organ that produces hormones X and Y.

_____   1

(iii) Explain how negative feedback is involved in the homeostatic control of blood glucose concentration.

_____

_____

_____   2

Marks

14. (*a*)   The diagram shows some plant communities present at various time intervals on farmland cleared of vegetation by a fire.

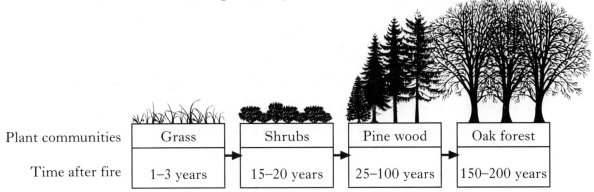

Plant communities	Grass	Shrubs	Pine wood	Oak forest
Time after fire	1–3 years	15–20 years	25–100 years	150–200 years

(i)   State the term used to describe this sequence of plant communities.

_____   1

(ii)   Give a reason to explain why the shrub community is able to replace the grass community after 15 years.

_____   1

(iii)   Oak forest is the climax community in this sequence.
Describe a feature of a climax community.

_____   1

(*b*)   The grid shows factors that can influence population change.

A competition	B predation	C rainfall
D disease	E temperature	F food supply

(i)   Use **all** the letters from the grid to complete the table to show which factors are density dependent and which are density independent.

Density dependent	*Density independent*

2

(ii)   **Underline** one alternative in each pair to make the sentences correct.

As population density $\left\{ \begin{array}{l} \text{increases,} \\ \text{decreases,} \end{array} \right\}$ the effect of density dependent factors increases.

As a result, the population density then $\left\{ \begin{array}{l} \text{increases} \\ \text{decreases} \end{array} \right\}$.   1

[Turn over for Section C on *Page thirty*

SECTION C

Marks

Both questions in this section should be attempted.

Note that each question contains a choice.

Questions 1 and 2 should be attempted on the blank pages which follow.

Supplementary sheets, if required, may be obtained from the invigilator.

All answers must be written clearly and legibly in ink.

Labelled diagrams may be used where appropriate.

1. Answer **either** A **or** B.

    A.   Give an account of respiration under the following headings:

        (i)   glycolysis;   **5**

        (ii)   the Krebs (Citric acid) cycle.   **5**

                                                     (10)

    OR

    B.   Give an account of cellular defence mechanisms in animals under the following headings:

        (i)   phagocytosis;   **4**

        (ii)   antibody production and tissue rejection.   **6**

                                                     (10)

In question 2, ONE mark is available for coherence and ONE mark is available for relevance.

2. Answer **either** A **or** B.

    A.   Give an account of the problems of osmoregulation in freshwater bony fish and outline their adaptations to overcome these problems.   **(10)**

    OR

    B.   Give an account of obtaining food in animals by reference to co-operative hunting, dominance hierarchy, and territorial behaviour.   **(10)**

[END OF QUESTION PAPER]

SPACE FOR ANSWERS

SPACE FOR ANSWERS

SPACE FOR ANSWERS

SPACE FOR ANSWERS

Page thirty-four

DO NOT
WRITE IN
THIS
MARGIN

SPACE FOR ANSWERS

SPACE FOR ANSWERS

ADDITIONAL GRAPH PAPER FOR QUESTION 10(*b*)

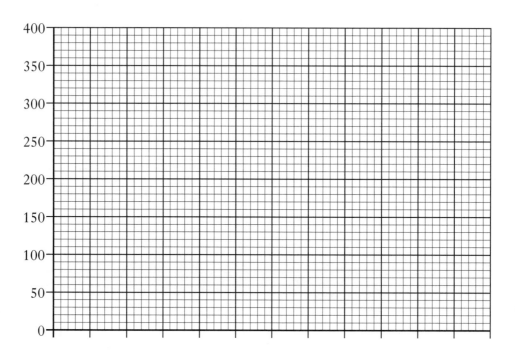

HIGHER

2008

[BLANK PAGE]

FOR OFFICIAL USE

Total for Sections B and C

X007/301

NATIONAL
QUALIFICATIONS
2008

TUESDAY, 27 MAY
1.00 PM – 3.30 PM

BIOLOGY
HIGHER

Fill in these boxes and read what is printed below.

Full name of centre

Town

Forename(s)

Surname

Date of birth
Day Month Year   Scottish candidate number   Number of seat

SECTION A–Questions 1—30 (30 marks)

Instructions for completion of Section A are given on page two.

For this section of the examination you must use an **HB pencil**.

SECTIONS B AND C (100 marks)

1   (a) All questions should be attempted.

    (b) It should be noted that in **Section C** questions 1 and 2 each contain a choice.

2   The questions may be answered in any order but all answers are to be written in the spaces provided in this answer book, **and must be written clearly and legibly in ink**.

3   Additional space for answers will be found at the end of the book. If further space is required, supplementary sheets may be obtained from the invigilator and should be inserted inside the **front cover** of this book.

4   The numbers of questions must be clearly inserted with any answers written in the additional space.

5   Rough work, if any should be necessary, should be written in this book and then scored through when the fair copy has been written. If further space is required a supplementary sheet for rough work may be obtained from the invigilator.

6   Before leaving the examination room you must give this book to the invigilator. If you do not, you may lose all the marks for this paper.

Read carefully

1   Check that the answer sheet provided is for **Biology Higher (Section A)**.

2   For this section of the examination you must use an **HB pencil**, and where necessary, an eraser.

3   Check that the answer sheet you have been given has **your name**, **date of birth**, **SCN** (Scottish Candidate Number) and **Centre Name** printed on it.

    Do not change any of these details.

4   If any of this information is wrong, tell the Invigilator immediately.

5   If this information is correct, **print** your name and seat number in the boxes provided.

6   The answer to each question is **either** A, B, C or D. Decide what your answer is, then, using your pencil, put a horizontal line in the space provided (see sample question below).

7   There is **only one correct** answer to each question.

8   Any rough working should be done on the question paper or the rough working sheet, **not** on your answer sheet.

9   At the end of the exam, put the **answer sheet for Section A inside the front cover of this answer book**.

Sample Question

The apparatus used to determine the energy stored in a foodstuff is a

A   calorimeter

B   respirometer

C   klinostat

D   gas burette.

The correct answer is **A**—calorimeter. The answer **A** has been clearly marked in **pencil** with a horizontal line (see below).

Changing an answer

If you decide to change your answer, carefully erase your first answer and using your pencil fill in the answer you want. The answer below has been changed to **D**.

SECTION A

All questions in this section should be attempted.

Answers should be given on the separate answer sheet provided.

1. The following statements relate to respiration and the mitochondrion.

    1   Glycolysis takes place in the mitochondrion.

    2   The mitochondrion has two membranes.

    3   The rate of respiration is affected by temperature.

    Which of the above statements are correct?

    A   1 and 2

    B   1 and 3

    C   2 and 3

    D   All of them

2. The anaerobic breakdown of glucose splits from the aerobic pathway of respiration

    A   after the formation of pyruvic acid

    B   after the formation of acetyl-CoA

    C   after the formation of citric acid

    D   at the start of glycolysis.

3. Phagocytes contain many lysosomes so that

    A   enzymes which destroy bacteria can be stored

    B   toxins from bacteria can be neutralised

    C   antibodies can be released in response to antigens

    D   bacteria can be engulfed into the cytoplasm.

4. After an animal cell is immersed in a hypotonic solution it will

    A   burst

    B   become turgid

    C   shrink

    D   become flaccid.

5. Which of the following proteins has a fibrous structure?

    A   Pepsin

    B   Amylase

    C   Insulin

    D   Collagen

6. The following cell components are involved in the synthesis and secretion of an enzyme.

    1   Golgi apparatus

    2   Ribosome

    3   Cytoplasm

    4   Endoplasmic reticulum

    Which of the following identifies correctly the route taken by an amino acid molecule as it passes through these cell components?

    A   3 2 1 4

    B   2 4 3 1

    C   3 2 4 1

    D   3 4 2 1

[Turn over

7. The graphs show the effect of various factors on the rate of uptake of chloride ions by discs of carrot tissue from their surrounding solution.

1

2

3

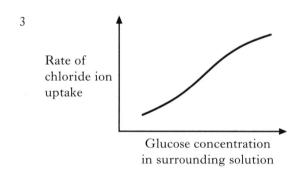

Which graphs support the hypothesis that chloride ion uptake by carrot tissue involves active transport?

A   1 and 2 only

B   1 and 3 only

C   2 and 3 only

D   1, 2 and 3

8. The R_f value of a pigment can be calculated as follows:

$$R_f = \frac{\text{distance travelled by pigment from origin}}{\text{distance travelled by solvent from origin}}$$

The diagram shows a chromatogram in which four chlorophyll pigments have been separated.

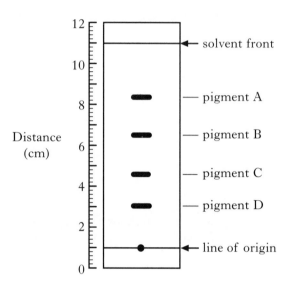

Which pigment has an R_f value of 0·2?

9. The following steps occur during the replication of a virus.

1   alteration of host cell metabolism

2   production of viral protein coats

3   replication of viral nucleic acid

In which sequence do these events occur?

A   1, 3, 2

B   1, 2, 3

C   2, 1, 3

D   3, 1, 2

10. The graphs below show the effect of two injections of an antigen on the formation of an antibody.

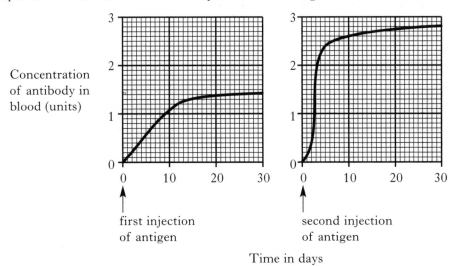

Concentration
of antibody in
blood (units)

first injection
of antigen

second injection
of antigen

Time in days

The concentration of antibodies is measured 25 days after each injection. The effect of the second injection is to increase the concentration by

A   1%

B   25%

C   50%

D   100%.

11. The diagram shows a stage of meiosis.

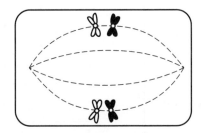

Which of the following diagrams shows the next stage in meiosis?

A

B

C

D
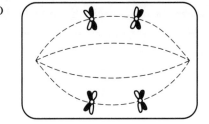

12. Cystic fibrosis is a genetic condition caused by an allele that is not sex-linked. A child is born with cystic fibrosis despite neither parent having the condition. The parents are going to have a second child.

What is the chance that the second child will have cystic fibrosis?

A 75%

B 67%

C 50%

D 25%

13. A sex-linked condition in humans is caused by a recessive allele.

An unaffected man and a carrier woman produce a son.

What is the chance that he will be unaffected?

A 1 in 1

B 1 in 2

C 1 in 3

D 1 in 4

14. A new species of organism is considered to have evolved when its population

A is isolated from the rest of the population by a geographical barrier

B shows increased variation due to mutations

C can no longer interbreed successfully with the rest of the population

D is subjected to increased selection pressure in its habitat.

15. The melanic variety of the peppered moth became common in industrial areas of Britain following the increase in the production of soot during the industrial revolution.

The increase in the melanic variety was due to

A melanic moths migrating to areas which gave the best camouflage

B a change in selection pressure

C an increase in the mutation rate

D a change in the prey species taken by birds.

16. Which of the following is true of freshwater fish?

A The kidneys contain few small glomeruli.

B The blood filtration rate is high.

C Concentrated urine is produced.

D The chloride secretory cells actively excrete excess salts.

17. Which of the following is a behavioural adaptation used by some mammals to survive in hot deserts?

A Dry mouth and nasal passages

B High levels of anti-diuretic hormone in the blood

C Very long kidney tubules

D Nocturnal habit

18. Which line in the table below correctly identifies the effect of the state of the guard cells on the opening and closing of stomata?

	State of guard cells	Stomata open/closed
A	flaccid	open
B	plasmolysed	open
C	flaccid	closed
D	turgid	closed

19. In an animal, habituation has taken place when a

A harmful stimulus ceases to produce a response

B harmful stimulus always produces an identical response

C harmless stimulus ceases to produce a response

D harmless stimulus always produces an identical response.

20. The table below shows the rate of production of urine by a salmon in both fresh and sea water.

	Rate of urine production (cm³/kg of body mass/hour)
In fresh water	5·0
In sea water	0·5

After transfer from the sea to fresh water, the volume of urine produced by a 2·5 kg salmon over a one hour period would have increased by

A   4·50 cm³

B   5·50 cm³

C   11·25 cm³

D   12·50 cm³.

21. A 30 g serving of a breakfast cereal contains 1·5 mg of iron. Only 25% of this iron is absorbed into the bloodstream.

If a pregnant woman requires a daily uptake of 6 mg of iron, how much cereal would she have to eat each day to meet this requirement?

A   60 g

B   120 g

C   240 g

D   480 g

22. Which of the following graphs represents the growth pattern of a locust?

A

B

C

D

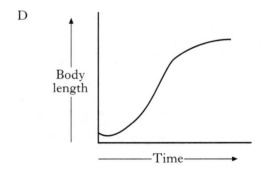

[Turn over

23. Gene expression in cells results in the synthesis of specific proteins. The process of transcription involved in the synthesis of a protein is the

A   production of a specific mRNA

B   processing of a specific mRNA on the ribosomes

C   replication of DNA in the nucleus

D   transfer of amino acids to the ribosomes.

24. Hormones P and Q are involved in the control of growth and metabolism.

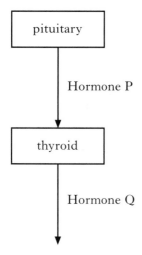

Control of growth and metabolism

Which line in the table below correctly identifies hormones P and Q?

	Hormone P	*Hormone Q*
A	TSH	growth hormone
B	thyroxine	TSH
C	TSH	thyroxine
D	growth hormone	TSH

25. Temperature control mechanisms in the skin of mammals are stimulated by

A   nerve impulses from the pituitary gland

B   nerve impulses from the hypothalamus

C   hormonal messages from the hypothalamus

D   hormonal messages from the pituitary gland.

26. Which of the following is **not** an effect of IAA?

A   Increased stem elongation

B   Fruit formation

C   Inhibition of leaf abscission

D   Initiation of germination

27. List P gives reasons why population monitoring may be carried out.

List Q gives three species whose populations are monitored by scientists.

List P	List Q
1 Valuable food resource	W Stonefly
2 Endangered species	X Humpback Whale
3 Indicator species	Y Haddock

Which line in the table below correctly matches reasons from **List P** with species from **List Q**?

	Reasons		
	1	2	3
A	W	X	Y
B	Y	W	X
C	X	Y	W
D	Y	X	W

28. The graph below records the body temperature of a woman during an investigation in which her arm was immersed in water.

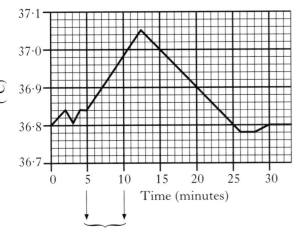

Arm immersed in water during this period

By how much did the temperature of her body vary during the 30 minutes of the investigation?

A   0·25 °C

B   0·27 °C

C   2·5 °C

D   2·7 °C

29. The graph below shows the variation in numbers of a predator and its prey recorded over a ten week period.

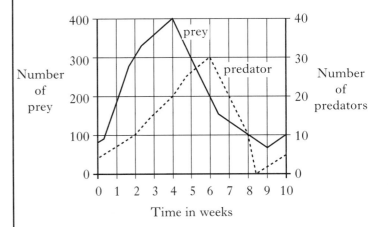

In which week is the prey to predator ratio the largest?

A   week 2

B   week 4

C   week 6

D   week 8

30. The graph below shows the length of a human fetus before birth.

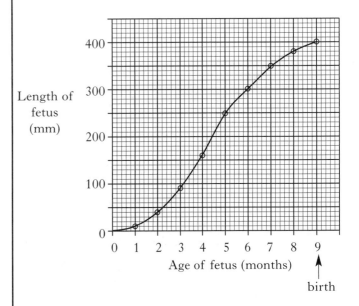

What is the percentage increase in length of the fetus during the 4 months before birth?

A   33·3%

B   37·5%

C   60·0%

D   150%

Candidates are reminded that the answer sheet MUST be returned INSIDE the front cover of this answer book.

Marks

SECTION B

All questions in this section should be attempted.

All answers must be written clearly and legibly in ink.

1. The diagram shows a chloroplast from a palisade mesophyll cell.

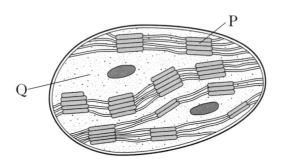

(a) Name regions P and Q.

P _____

Q _____   1

(b)   (i) Mark an X on the diagram to show the location of chlorophyll molecules.   1

     (ii) As well as chlorophyll, plants have other photosynthetic pigments.

           State the benefit to plants of having these other pigments.

           _____

           _____   1

(c)   (i) Name **one** product of the light dependent stage of photosynthesis which is required for the carbon fixation stage (Calvin cycle).

           _____   1

     (ii) The table shows some substances involved in the carbon fixation stage of photosynthesis.

           Complete the table by inserting the number of carbon atoms present in one molecule of each substance.

Substance	Number of carbon atoms in one molecule
Glucose	
Carbon dioxide	
Glycerate phosphate (GP)	
Ribulose bisphosphate (RuBP)	

2

Marks

1. **(continued)**

(*d*) The graph below shows the effect of increasing light intensity on the rate of photosynthesis at different carbon dioxide concentrations and temperatures.

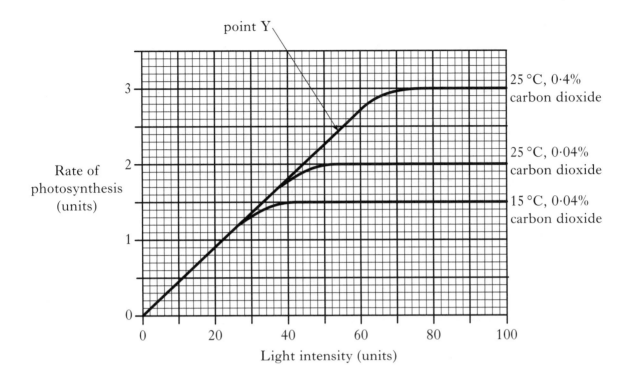

(i) Identify the factor limiting the rate of photosynthesis at point Y on the graph.

_____   1

(ii) From the graph, identify the factor that has the greatest effect in increasing the rate of photosynthesis at a light intensity of 80 units.

Justify your answer.

Factor _____

Justification _____

_____

_____   1

[Turn over

2.   The diagram shows a human liver cell and a magnified section of its plasma membrane.

Marks

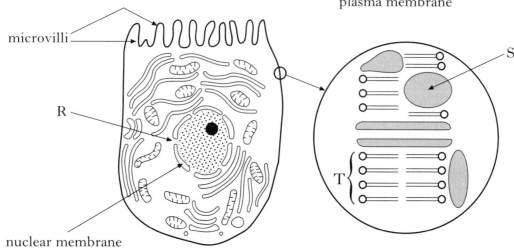

(a)   (i)   Identify molecules S and T.

S ———————————————   1

T———————————————   1

(ii)   A pore in the nuclear membrane is shown by label R.

Describe the importance of these pores in protein synthesis.

———————————————————————————————

———————————————————————————————   1

(iii)   What evidence in the diagram suggests that this cell produces large quantities of ATP?

———————————————————————————————   1

Marks

2. **(continued)**

(*b*) Some liver cells take up glucose from the blood by the process of diffusion.

(i) Describe this process.

_____

_____ 1

(ii) Suggest a reason for the presence of microvilli in liver cells as shown in the diagram.

_____

_____

_____ 2

(iii) Glucose taken up by liver cells can be converted into a storage carbohydrate.

Name this carbohydrate.

_____ 1

[Turn over

Marks

3. Fat can be used as an alternative respiratory substrate. The diagram shows the breakdown of fat in an athlete's muscle cells during the final stages of a marathon race.

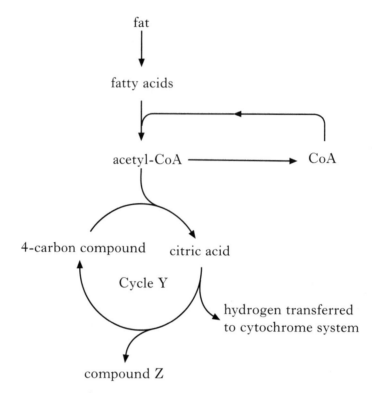

(a) Name a respiratory substrate, other than fat, which can be used by muscle cells.

_____ 1

(b) (i) Name cycle Y and compound Z.

Cycle Y _____

Compound Z _____ 1

(ii) Name the carrier that accepts and transfers hydrogen to the cytochrome system.

_____ 1

(c) Describe the role of oxygen in aerobic respiration.

_____

_____ 1

Marks

3. **(continued)**

(*d*) During an 800 metre race, an athlete's muscle cells may respire anaerobically to produce ATP.

(i) State **one** other metabolic product of anaerobic respiration in muscle cells.

_____ 1

(ii) Where in a cell does anaerobic respiration occur?

_____ 1

(iii) Describe the importance of ATP to cells.

_____

_____ 1

[Turn over

Marks

4. (*a*) Decide if each of the following statements about DNA replication is **True** or **False** and tick (✓) the appropriate box.

If the statement is False, write the correct word in the correction box to replace the word <u>underlined</u> in the statement.

Statement	True	False	Correction
During DNA replication <u>hydrogen</u> bonds between bases break.			
During the formation of a new DNA molecule, base pairing is followed by bonding between deoxyribose and <u>bases</u>.			
As a result of DNA replication, the DNA content of a cell is <u>halved</u>.			

2

(*b*) Free DNA nucleotides are needed for DNA replication.

Name **one** other substance that is needed for DNA replication.

_____ 1

(*c*) A single strand of a DNA molecule has 6000 nucleotides of which 24% are adenine and 18% are cytosine.

(i) Calculate the combined percentage of thymine and guanine bases on the same DNA strand.

Space for calculation

_____ % 1

(ii) How many guanine bases would be present on the complementary strand of this DNA molecule?

Space for calculation

_____ bases 1

Marks

5. Ponderosa pine trees produce resin following damage to their bark.

In an investigation, three individual pine trees were chosen from areas with different population densities. Each tree was damaged by having a hole bored through its bark.

Measurements of resin production from each hole following this damage are shown in the table.

Population density (Number of trees per hectare)	Volume of resin produced in the first day (cm³)	Duration of resin flow (days)	Total volume of resin produced (cm³)
2	8·3	7·0	29·3
10	0·8	4·8	2·9
50	0·6	4·6	2·8

(a) (i) Describe how population density affects the total volume of resin produced.

_____

_____

_____   2

(ii) Calculate the average resin flow per day at a population density of 2 trees per hectare **after the first day**.

Space for calculation

_____ cm³ per day   1

(b) Explain how resin production protects trees.

_____

_____   1

[Turn over

6. An investigation was carried out to compare the rates of water loss from tree species during winter when soil water availability is low.

    The table shows information about the tree species involved.

Tree species	Leaf type	Leaves lost in winter
cherry laurel	broad	no
white oak	broad	yes
loblolly pine	needle-like	no

One year old trees of each species were grown outside in identical environmental conditions during winter. The average rate of water loss from each species was measured every tenth day over a 70 day period.

The results are shown in **Graph 1**.

Graph 1

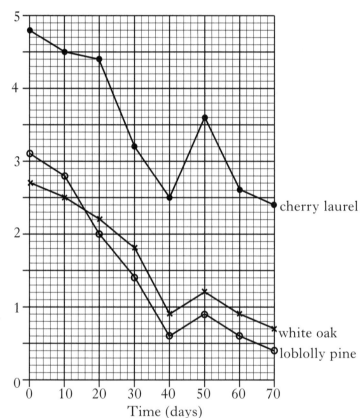

(a) (i) **Use values from Graph 1** to describe the changes in rate of water loss from loblolly pine over the 70 day period.

    _____

    _____

    _____   2

    (ii) Calculate the percentage decrease in rate of water loss from cherry laurel between day 0 and day 50.

    Space for calculation

    _____ %   1

Marks

6. **(a)** **(continued)**

    (iii) **From Graph 1** express, as the simplest whole number ratio, the rates of water loss from white oak and cherry laurel on day 20.

          _____ white oak : _____ cherry laurel   1

    (iv) Using the information from the table **and** from Graph 1, suggest the advantage to the white oak of losing its leaves in winter.

        Justify your answer.

        Advantage _____

        Justification _____

        _____

        _____   2

(b) In a further investigation, the effect of air temperature on the average rate of water loss from loblolly pine was measured.

The results are shown in **Graph 2**.

Graph 2

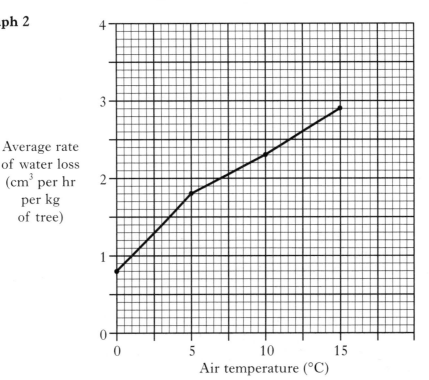

    (i) Use the information from **Graphs 1 and 2** to suggest the air temperature on day 30 of the investigation.

                                        _____ °C   1

    (ii) Predict the rate of water loss from loblolly pine at an air temperature of 18 °C.

        _____ cm³ per hour per kg of tree.   1

    (iii) Apart from air temperature and soil water availability, state **one** factor which can affect water loss from trees.

        _____   1

Marks

7. In horses, coat colour is determined by two genes. The allele for black coat (**B**) is dominant to the allele for chestnut coat (**b**). The allele for grey coat (**G**) is dominant to the allele for non-grey coat (**g**).

   Horses with the allele **G** are **always** grey.

   A male with the genotype **GgBb** was crossed with a female with the genotype **ggBb**.

   (*a*) (i) State the phenotype of each parent.

   Male   _____

   Female   _____   1

   (ii) Complete the grid by adding the genotypes of:

   1 the male and female gametes;   1

   2 the possible offspring.   1

	Male gametes		
Female gametes			

   (iii) Give the expected phenotype ratio of the offspring from this cross.

   _____ Grey : _____ Black : _____ Chestnut   1

   (*b*) A further gene determines the presence of large white markings in the coat. The allele for the presence of white markings (**T**) is dominant to the allele for their absence (**t**).

   A breeder found that a male horse with white markings always produced offspring with white markings when crossed with a female of any phenotype.

   Explain this observation in terms of the genotype of this male horse.

   _____

   _____   1

Marks

8. Grey wolves hunt in packs. Their prey includes a variety of large herbivores.

   (a) (i) Name the hunting method used by wolves and state **one** advantage of this method.

   Name _____ 1

   Advantage _____

   _____ 1

   (ii) Following the capture of prey, higher ranking wolves feed first.

   State the term which describes this type of social organisation.

   _____ 1

   (iii) Wolf packs occupy territories ranging from 80 to $1500\,\text{km}^2$.

   1 Describe **one** advantage to the wolf pack of occupying a territory.

   _____

   _____ 1

   2 Suggest **one** factor that could influence the size of a territory occupied by a wolf pack.

   _____ 1

   (b) The grey wolf was once common in North America but is now an endangered species in many areas.

   Following steps to conserve the species, wolf numbers in one wildlife reserve increased from 31 to 683 individuals during an eight year period.

   (i) Calculate the average yearly increase in wolf numbers during this period.

   Space for calculation

   _____ per year 1

   (ii) Other than wildlife reserves, describe **one** method used to conserve endangered species.

   _____ 1

   [Turn over

Marks

9. Beech trees have two types of leaf. Sun leaves are exposed to high light intensities for most of the day and shade leaves are usually overshadowed by sun leaves.

   The rates of carbon dioxide exchange at different light intensities were measured for sun leaves and shade leaves from one beech tree.

   The results are shown on the graph.

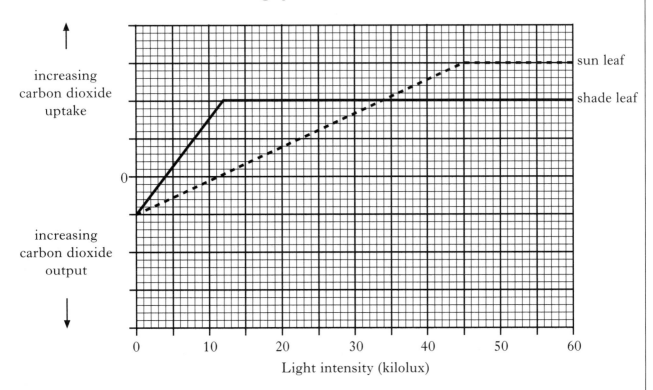

   (a) State the light intensity at which the shade leaves reach their compensation point.

   _____ kilolux   **1**

   (b) Explain why having shade leaves is an advantage to a beech tree.

   _____

   _____   **1**

Marks

10. Camels live in deserts where temperatures rise to 50 °C during the day and fall to minus 10 °C at night. The graph shows how the body temperature of a camel varied over a three day period.

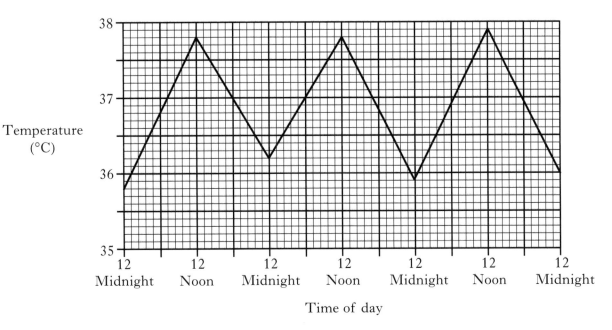

(a) From the information given, what evidence is there that camels obtain heat from their own metabolism?

_____

_____   1

(b) What term is used for animals that obtain most of their body heat from their own metabolism?

_____   1

[Turn over

11. In an investigation into the effect of potassium on barley root growth, twelve *Marks* containers were set up as shown.

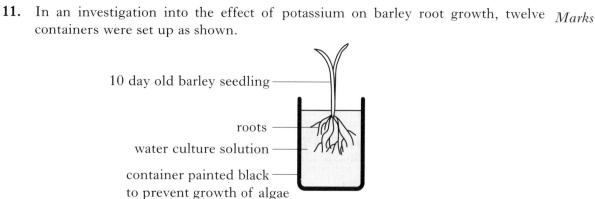

10 day old barley seedling

roots

water culture solution

container painted black
to prevent growth of algae

The water culture solution provided all the elements needed for normal growth.

In six of the containers, the potassium concentration was 2 micromoles per litre. In the other six containers, the potassium concentration was 5 millimoles per litre.

The containers were kept at 20 °C and in constant light intensity.

Every three days, the roots from one container at each potassium concentration were harvested and their dry mass measured.

(a) How many times greater was the potassium concentration in the 5 millimoles per litre solution than in the 2 micromoles per litre solution?

   1 millimole per litre = 1000 micromoles per litre

   Space for calculation

   _____ times   **1**

(b) (i) Identify **one** variable, not already described, that should be kept constant.

   _____   **1**

   (ii) Suggest **one** advantage of growing the seedlings in water culture solutions rather than soil.

   _____   **1**

   (iii) Complete the table to give the reasons for each experimental procedure.

Experimental procedure	Reason
paint containers black to prevent growth of algae	
measure dry mass rather than fresh mass of roots	

2

11. (continued)

(c) The results of the investigation are shown in the table.

Time (days)	Dry mass of roots (mg)	
	Potassium concentration 2 micromoles per litre	Potassium concentration 5 millimoles per litre
3	1	1
6	5	6
9	8	10
12	11	14
15	16	22
18	22	44

The results for the seedlings grown in 5 millimoles potassium per litre solution are shown on the graph.

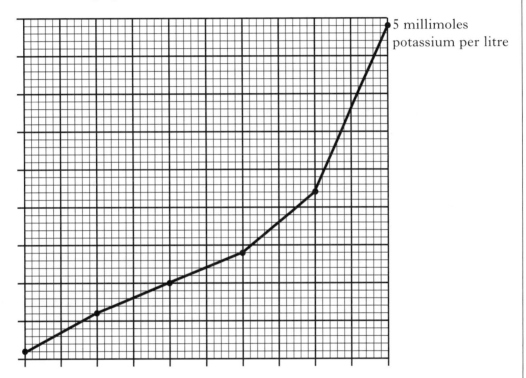

Complete the graph by:

(i) adding the scale and label to each axis;　　　　1

(ii) presenting the results for the 2 micromoles potassium per litre solution **and** labelling the line.　　　　1

(Additional graph paper, if required, will be found on page 36.)

(d) In a further experiment, bubbling oxygen through the water culture solutions was observed to increase the uptake of potassium by the barley roots.

Explain this observation.

_____

_____

_____　　　　2

Marks

12. The diagram shows a section through a three year old hawthorn twig with annual rings.

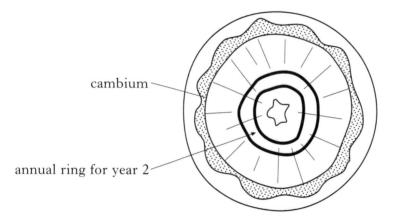

cambium

annual ring for year 2

(a) (i) State the function of cambium.

_____   1

(ii) Name the tissue of which annual rings are composed.

_____   1

(b) The tree suffered an infestation of leaf-eating caterpillars during year 2.

Explain how an infestation of leaf-eating caterpillars could account for the narrow appearance of this annual ring.

_____

_____

_____   2

Marks

13. The flow chart shows part of the homeostatic control of water concentration in human blood.

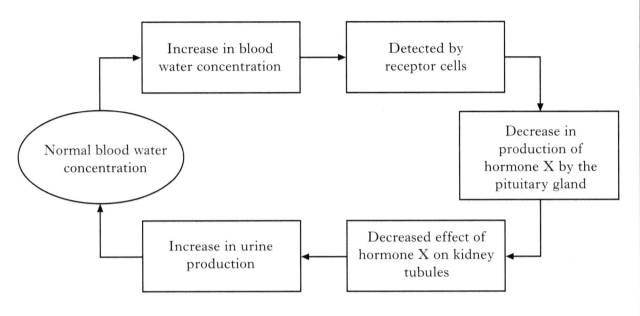

(a) (i) Suggest a reason for the increase in blood water concentration.

_____ 1

(ii) State the location of the receptor cells.

_____ 1

(iii) Name hormone X and state its effect on the kidney tubules.

Name _____ 1

Effect _____

_____ 1

(b) Control of water concentration in human blood involves negative feedback. Explain what is meant by negative feedback.

_____

_____

_____ 2

[Turn over

Marks

14. Frequency of mating in a population of wild goats was observed from June to November.

The results are shown in the table.

Month	Average number of hours of light per day	Frequency of mating 0 = no mating + = occasional mating ++ = frequent mating
June	19	0
July	17	0
August	15	0
September	13	+
October	11	++
November	9	++

(a) Using the information given, identify the trigger stimulus which results in mating of goats.

_____   1

(b) Young goats are born 5 months after mating.

Explain how the pattern of mating frequency shown increases the survival rate of the offspring.

_____

_____

_____   2

(c) What general term is used to describe the effect of light on the timing of breeding in mammals such as goats?

_____   1

SECTION C

Marks

Both questions in this section should be attempted.

Note that each question contains a choice.

Questions 1 and 2 should be attempted on the blank pages which follow.

Supplementary sheets, if required, may be obtained from the invigilator.

All answers must be written clearly and legibly in ink.

Labelled diagrams may be used where appropriate.

1. Answer **either** A **or** B.

   A. Write notes on:

(i)	the control of lactose metabolism in *E. coli*;	**6**
(ii)	phenylketonuria in humans.	**4**
		(10)

   OR

   B. Write notes on population change under the following headings:

(i)	the influence of density dependent factors;	**5**
(ii)	succession in plant communities.	**5**
		(10)

In question 2, ONE mark is available for coherence and ONE mark is available for relevance.

2. Answer **either** A **or** B.

   A. Give an account of gene mutations and mutagenic agents. **(10)**

   OR

   B. Give an account of somatic fusion in plants and genetic engineering in bacteria. **(10)**

[END OF QUESTION PAPER]

SPACE FOR ANSWERS

Page thirty

SPACE FOR ANSWERS

SPACE FOR ANSWERS

SPACE FOR ANSWERS

SPACE FOR ANSWERS

SPACE FOR ANSWERS

SPACE FOR ANSWERS

ADDITIONAL GRAPH PAPER FOR QUESTION 11(*c*)

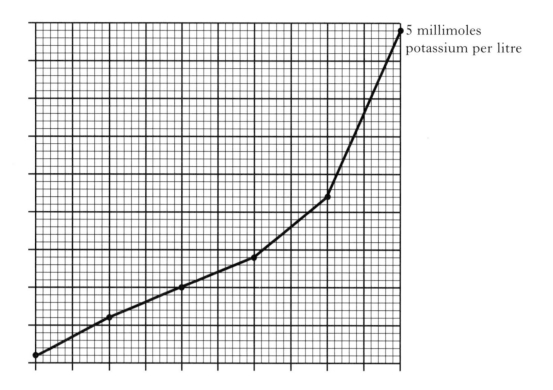

5 millimoles
potassium per litre

[BLANK PAGE]

FOR OFFICIAL USE

Total for
Sections
B and C

X007/301

NATIONAL
QUALIFICATIONS
2009

THURSDAY, 28 MAY
1.00 PM – 3.30 PM

BIOLOGY
HIGHER

Fill in these boxes and read what is printed below.

Full name of centre

Town

Forename(s)

Surname

Date of birth
Day Month Year

Scottish candidate number

Number of seat

SECTION A–Questions 1—30 (30 marks)

Instructions for completion of Section A are given on page two.

For this section of the examination you must use an **HB pencil**.

SECTIONS B AND C (100 marks)

1 (a) All questions should be attempted.

   (b) It should be noted that in **Section C** questions 1 and 2 each contain a choice.

2 The questions may be answered in any order but all answers are to be written in the spaces provided in this answer book, **and must be written clearly and legibly in ink**.

3 Additional space for answers will be found at the end of the book. If further space is required, supplementary sheets may be obtained from the invigilator and should be inserted inside the **front cover** of this book.

4 The numbers of questions must be clearly inserted with any answers written in the additional space.

5 Rough work, if any should be necessary, should be written in this book and then scored through when the fair copy has been written. If further space is required a supplementary sheet for rough work may be obtained from the invigilator.

6 Before leaving the examination room you must give this book to the invigilator. If you do not, you may lose all the marks for this paper.

Read carefully

1   Check that the answer sheet provided is for **Biology Higher (Section A)**.

2   For this section of the examination you must use an **HB pencil**, and where necessary, an eraser.

3   Check that the answer sheet you have been given has **your name**, **date of birth**, **SCN** (Scottish Candidate Number) and **Centre Name** printed on it.

    Do not change any of these details.

4   If any of this information is wrong, tell the Invigilator immediately.

5   If this information is correct, **print** your name and seat number in the boxes provided.

6   The answer to each question is **either** A, B, C or D. Decide what your answer is, then, using your pencil, put a horizontal line in the space provided (see sample question below).

7   There is **only one correct** answer to each question.

8   Any rough working should be done on the question paper or the rough working sheet, **not** on your answer sheet.

9   At the end of the exam, put the **answer sheet for Section A inside the front cover of this answer book**.

Sample Question

The apparatus used to determine the energy stored in a foodstuff is a

A   calorimeter

B   respirometer

C   klinostat

D   gas burette.

The correct answer is **A**—calorimeter. The answer **A** has been clearly marked in **pencil** with a horizontal line (see below).

Changing an answer

If you decide to change your answer, carefully erase your first answer and using your pencil fill in the answer you want. The answer below has been changed to **D**.

SECTION A

All questions in this section should be attempted.

Answers should be given on the separate answer sheet provided.

1. Which of the following is **not** surrounded by a membrane?

   A   Nucleus

   B   Ribosome

   C   Chloroplast

   D   Mitochondrion

2. The diagram below shows a plant cell which has been placed in a salt solution.

   Which line in the table describes correctly the salt solution and the state of the plant cell?

	Salt solution	State of cell
A	hypertonic	plasmolysed
B	hypertonic	turgid
C	hypotonic	flaccid
D	hypotonic	plasmolysed

3. Thin sections of beetroot and rhubarb tissue were immersed in the same sucrose solution for the same time. This resulted in the plasmolysis of 0% of the beetroot cells and 20% of the rhubarb cells.

   Which of the following statements can be deduced from these results?

   A   The sucrose solution was hypertonic to the beetroot cells.

   B   The sucrose solution was hypotonic to the rhubarb cells.

   C   The contents of the beetroot cells were hypotonic to the contents of the rhubarb cells.

   D   The contents of the rhubarb cells were hypotonic to the contents of the beetroot cells.

4. The total sunlight energy landing on an ecosystem is 4 million kilojoules per square metre (kJm^{-2}). Four percent of this is fixed during photosynthesis and five percent of this fixed energy is passed on to the primary consumers. What is the energy intake of the primary consumers?

   A $800 \ kJm^{-2}$

   B $8000 \ kJm^{-2}$

   C $20\,000 \ kJm^{-2}$

   D $360\,000 \ kJm^{-2}$

5. The diagram below shows a chromatogram of four plant pigments.

   The R_f value of each is calculated by dividing the furthest distance the pigment has moved, by the distance the solvent has moved from the origin.

   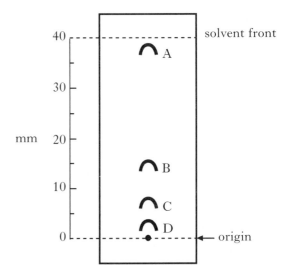

   Which pigment has an R_f value closest to 0·4?

[Turn over

6. The diagram below shows energy transfer within a cell.

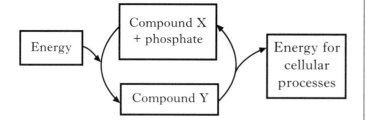

Which line in the table below identifies correctly compounds X and Y?

	X	Y
A	glucose	ATP
B	glucose	ADP
C	ADP	ATP
D	ATP	glucose

7. Which line in the table below shows correctly the sites of stages in aerobic respiration?

	Glycolysis	Krebs Cycle	Cytochrome System
A	Cristae of Mitochondrion	Matrix of Mitochondrion	Cytoplasm
B	Cytoplasm	Cristae of Mitochondrion	Matrix of Mitochondrion
C	Cytoplasm	Matrix of Mitochondrion	Cristae of Mitochondrion
D	Matrix of Mitochondrion	Cytoplasm	Cristae of Mitochondrion

8. Which of the following is **not** composed of amino acids?

A Glucagon

B Collagen

C Amylase

D Cellulose

9. The table below refers to the mass of DNA in certain human body cells.

Cell type	Mass of DNA in cell ($\times 10^{-12}$ g)
liver	6·6
lung	6·6
P	3·3
Q	0·0

Which of the following is most likely to identify correctly cell types P and Q?

	P	Q
A	kidney cell	sperm cell
B	sperm cell	mature red blood cell
C	mature red blood cell	sperm cell
D	nerve cell	mature red blood cell

10. Which line in the table below identifies correctly cellular defence mechanisms in plants which protect them against micro-organisms and herbivores?

	Defence against micro-organisms	Defence against herbivores
A	antibodies	resins
B	tannins	cyanide
C	spines	cyanide
D	resins	antibodies

11. In poultry, males have two X chromosomes and females have one X chromosome and one Y chromosome.

The gene for feather-barring is sex-linked.

The allele for barred feathers is dominant to the allele for non-barred feathers.

A non-barred male is crossed with a barred female.

What ratio of offspring would be expected?

A 1 barred male : 1 barred female

B 1 non-barred male : 1 non-barred female

C 1 barred male : 1 non-barred female

D 1 non-barred male : 1 barred female

12. The table below shows some genotypes and phenotypes associated with a form of anaemia.

Genotype	Phenotype
AA	Unaffected
AS	Sickle cell trait
SS	Acute sickle cell anaemia

A person with sickle cell trait and an unaffected person have a child together.

What are the chances of the child having acute sickle cell anaemia?

A none

B 1 in 4

C 1 in 2

D 1 in 1

13. Which of the following statements refers to a gene mutation?

A A change in the chromosome number caused by non-disjunction.

B A change in the number of genes on a chromosome caused by duplication.

C A change in the structure of a chromosome caused by translocation.

D A change in the base sequence of DNA caused by substitution.

14. Polyploidy in plants may result from

A total spindle failure during meiosis

B hybridisation between varieties of the same species

C homologous chromosomes binding at chiasmata

D the failure of linked genes to separate.

15. Which of the following is an example of artificial selection?

A Industrial melanism in moths

B DDT resistance in mosquitoes

C Increased milk yield in dairy cattle

D Decreasing effect of antibiotics on bacteria

16. The diagram below shows stages involved in the genetic engineering of bacteria to produce human insulin.

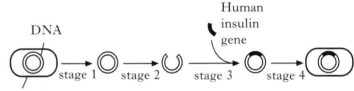

Which line in the table below shows the stages of this process in which endonuclease and ligase are involved?

	Stage involving endonuclease	Stage involving ligase
A	2	4
B	2	3
C	3	2
D	4	3

[Turn over

17. The statements below describe methods of maintaining a water balance in fish.

1   Salts actively absorbed by chloride secretory cells

2   Salts actively secreted by chloride secretory cells

3   Low rate of kidney filtration

4   High rate of kidney filtration

Which of these are used by **freshwater** bony fish?

A   1 and 3 only

B   2 and 4 only

C   1 and 4 only

D   2 and 3 only

18. The graph below shows the net energy gain or loss from hunting and eating prey of different masses.

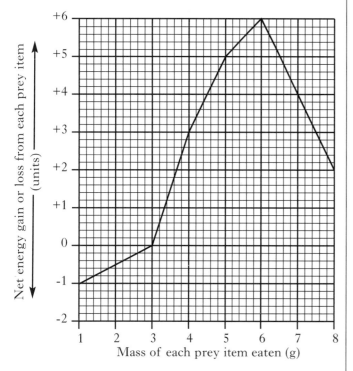

Mass of each prey item eaten (g)

It can be concluded from the graph that

A   prey between 1 g and 3 g are rarer than prey between 3 g and 6 g

B   hunting and eating prey above 6 g involves a net energy loss

C   prey of 8 g contain less energy than prey of mass 6 g

D   hunting and eating prey below 3 g involves a net energy loss.

19. Which of the following statements about habituation is correct?

A   It is a temporary change in behaviour.

B   It occurs only in young animals.

C   It is a social mechanism for defence.

D   It is a permanent change in behaviour.

20. Some animal species live in social groups for defence.

Which of the following statements describes a change which could result from an increase in the size of such a social group?

A   Individuals are able to spend less time feeding.

B   There are fewer times when more than one animal is looking for predators.

C   Each animal can spend more time looking for predators than foraging.

D   Individuals are able to spend less time looking for predators.

21. Phenylketonuria is a condition that results from

A   differential gene expression

B   chromosome non-disjunction

C   a vitamin deficiency

D   an inherited gene mutation.

22. The plant growth substance indole acetic acid (IAA) is of benefit to humans because it can function

A   as a herbicide and to break dormancy

B   as a herbicide and as a rooting powder

C   in the germination of barley and to break dormancy

D   as a rooting powder and in the germination of barley.

23. The graph below shows changes in the α-amylase concentration and starch content of a barley grain during early growth and development.

- - - - - - starch content

————— α-amylase concentration

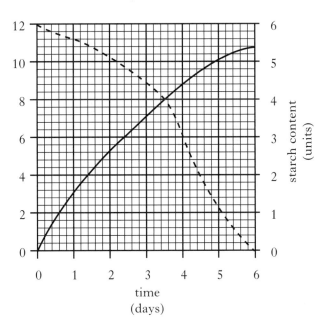

What is the α-amylase concentration when the starch content has decreased by 50%?

A 4·4 units

B 6·0 units

C 8·2 units

D 8·8 units

24. A species of plant was exposed to various periods of light and dark, after which its flowering response was observed.

The results are shown below.

Light period (hours)	Dark period (hours)	Flowering response
4	12	flowering
4	10	flowering
6	18	maximum flowering
14	10	flowering
18	9	no flowering
18	6	no flowering
18	10	flowering

What appears to be the critical factor which stimulates flowering?

A A minimum dark period of 10 hours

B A light/dark cycle of at least 24 hours

C A light period of less than 18 hours

D A dark period which exceeds the light period

25. When there is a decrease in the water concentration of the blood, which of the following series of events shows the negative feedback response of the body?

	Concentration of ADH	Permeability of kidney tubules	Volume of urine
A	increases	increases	increases
B	decreases	decreases	increases
C	increases	increases	decreases
D	decreases	increases	decreases

[Turn over

26. High levels of blood glucose can cause clouding of the lens in the human eye. Concentrations above 5·5 mM are believed to put the individual at a high risk of lens damage.

In an investigation, people of different ages each drank a glucose solution. The concentration of glucose in their blood was monitored over a number of hours. The results are shown in the graph below.

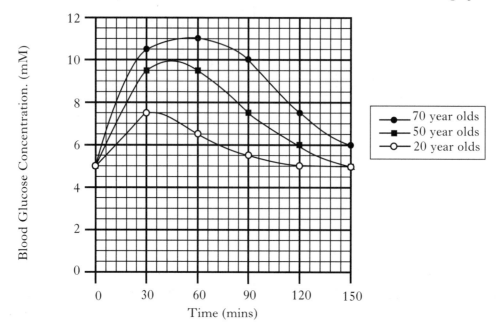

For how long during the investigation did 20 year olds remain above the high risk blood glucose concentration?

A   84 mins

B   90 mins

C   120 mins

D   148 mins

27. Which of the following shows correct responses to changes in sugar concentration in the blood?

	Sugar concentration in blood	Glucagon secretion	Insulin secretion	Glycogen stored in liver
A	increases	decreases	increases	increases
B	increases	decreases	increases	decreases
C	decreases	increases	decreases	increases
D	decreases	decreases	increases	decreases

28. A person produces 0·75 litres of urine in 24 hours. This urine contains 18 g of urea.

What is the concentration of urea in this urine?

A $1\cdot0\,g/100\,cm^3$

B $2\cdot4\,g/litre$

C $2\cdot4\,g/100\,cm^3$

D $3\cdot6\,g/100\,cm^3$

29. The list below describes changes involved in temperature regulation.

List

1 Increased vasodilation

2 Decreased vasodilation

3 Hair erector muscles contract

4 Hair erector muscles relax

Which of these are responses to cooling in mammals?

A 1 and 3 only

B 1 and 4 only

C 2 and 3 only

D 2 and 4 only

30. Which line in the table below shows correctly the main source of body heat and the method of controlling body temperature in an ectotherm?

	Main source of body heat	*Method of controlling body temperature*
A	Respiration	Physiological
B	Respiration	Behavioural
C	Absorbed from environment	Physiological
D	Absorbed from environment	Behavioural

Candidates are reminded that the answer sheet MUST be returned INSIDE the front cover of this answer book.

[Turn over

Marks

SECTION B

All questions in this section should be attempted.

All answers must be written clearly and legibly in ink.

1. (a) The diagram below shows light striking a green leaf.

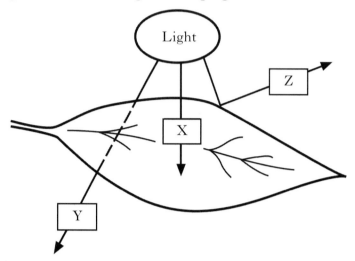

Arrow X shows light being absorbed.

State the terms used to describe what is happening to light at Y and Z.

Y _____

Z _____   1

(b) The diagram below represents the absorption of different colours of light by a photosynthetic pigment.

violet   blue   green   yellow   orange   red

colours of light

■ high absorption

▨ low absorption

(i) Name this photosynthetic pigment.

_____   1

(ii) State the role of accessory pigments in photosynthesis.

_____

_____   1

Marks

1. **(continued)**

   (*c*) The diagram below shows an outline of the carbon fixation stage of photosynthesis.

      (i) State the exact location of this stage in a plant cell.

      _____   **1**

      (ii) Describe the role of hydrogen in the carbon fixation stage.

      _____

      _____   **1**

   (*d*) The graph below shows the effect of increasing the concentration of carbon dioxide on the rate of photosynthesis by a plant at different temperatures.

   Light intensity was kept constant.

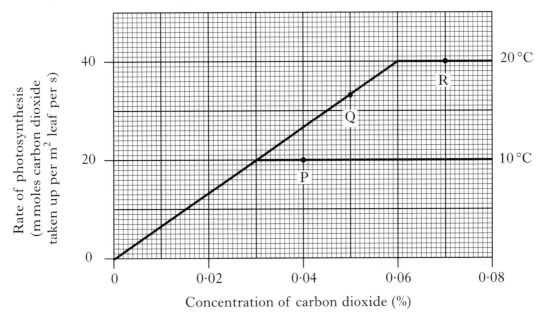

      Using the information in the graph, identify the factor which is limiting the rate of photosynthesis at each of the points P, Q and R.

      P _____

      Q _____

      R _____   **2**

Marks

2. (*a*) The diagram below shows some of the steps in respiration.

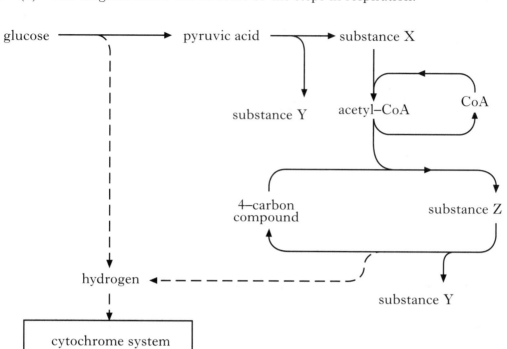

(i) Complete the table below by naming substances W, X and Y.

Substance	Name
W	
X	
Y	

2

(ii) State the number of carbon atoms present in a molecule of substance Z.

_____

1

Marks

2. **(continued)**

(b) Yeast cells were grown in both aerobic and anaerobic conditions and the volume of carbon dioxide produced was measured.

The results are shown in the graph below.

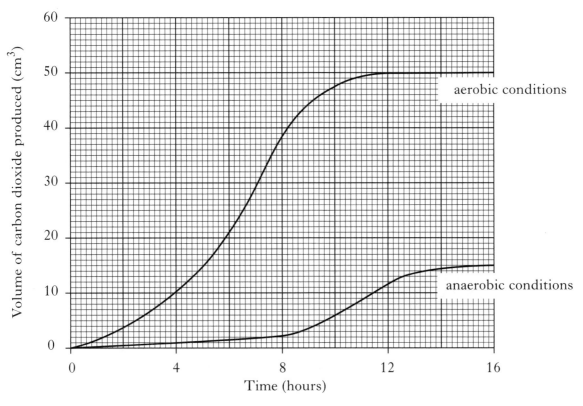

(i) At which time is there the greatest difference between the volumes of carbon dioxide produced in aerobic and anaerobic conditions?

Tick (✓) the correct box.

☐   ☐   ☐   ☐   ☐

8 hours   10 hours   12 hours   14 hours   16 hours   **1**

(ii) Calculate the average rate of carbon dioxide production per hour over the first 6 hours in aerobic conditions.

Space for calculation

_____ cm³ per hour   **1**

[Turn over

Marks

3. (*a*) The diagram below shows one stage in the synthesis of a protein at a ribosome.

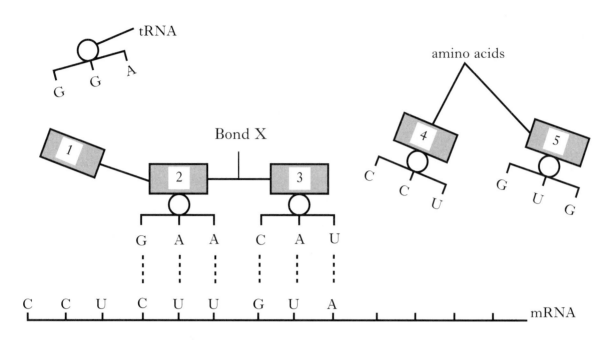

(i) Name this stage in protein synthesis.

_____ 1

(ii) Name bond X.

_____ 1

(iii) The table below shows five codons and their corresponding amino acids.

Codon	Amino acid
CUU	leucine
GGA	glycine
CAA	glutamic acid
GUA	valine
CCU	proline

Use information from the table to identify amino acids 1 and 4.

1 _____

4 _____ 1

Marks

3. **(continued)**

    (*b*) The diagram below shows a cell from the pancreas.

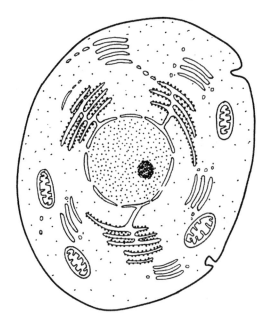

    What feature of this cell shows that it is involved in the secretion of protein?

    _____   **1**

[Turn over

Marks

4. (*a*) The diagram below shows some stages during the invasion of a cell by a virus.

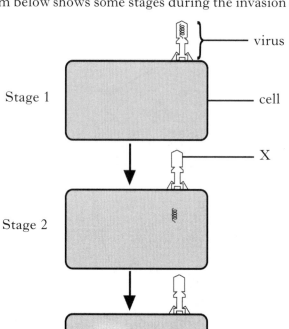

(i) Name the substance of which part X is composed.

_____   **1**

(ii) Describe what happens in the cell between stage 2 and stage 3 to allow the viral nucleic acid to replicate.

_____

_____   **1**

(iii) Describe **two** events which occur between stage 3 and the bursting of the cell to release new viruses.

1 _____

_____

2 _____

_____   **2**

Marks

4. (continued)

(*b*) The presence of viruses in the human body triggers antibody production by lymphocytes.

    (i) What name is given to any substance that triggers this response?

_____ **1**

    (ii) A person was injected with a vaccine on day 1 and again on day 36 of a 70 day study. The table below shows the concentration of antibodies to this vaccine in this person's blood at the end of each 7 day period during the study.

1st injection   2nd injection

Day	7	14	21	28	35	42	49	56	63	70
Concentration of antibody (mg/100 ml blood)	3	15	28	32	10	80	102	112	120	118

    1 How many times greater was the maximum antibody concentration following the second injection compared with the maximum concentration following the first?

    Space for calculation

_____ times **1**

    2 The second injection caused a higher concentration of antibody to be produced than the first injection.

    Identify **two** other differences in the response to the second injection.

    1 _____

    2 _____ **1**

[Turn over

5. Mexican spotted owls are territorial and prey on several species of small mammal. *Marks*
Three pairs of owls were studied over a two year period.

The table below shows the number of each prey species eaten by each pair of owls.

Prey species	Number of each prey species eaten by each pair of owls		
	Owl pair A	Owl pair B	Owl pair C
deer mouse	484	528	515
woodrat	29	144	141
brush mouse	15	114	118
rock squirrel	22	24	23

The graph below shows the average number and average total biomass of deer mice and woodrats living in the study area in different seasons.

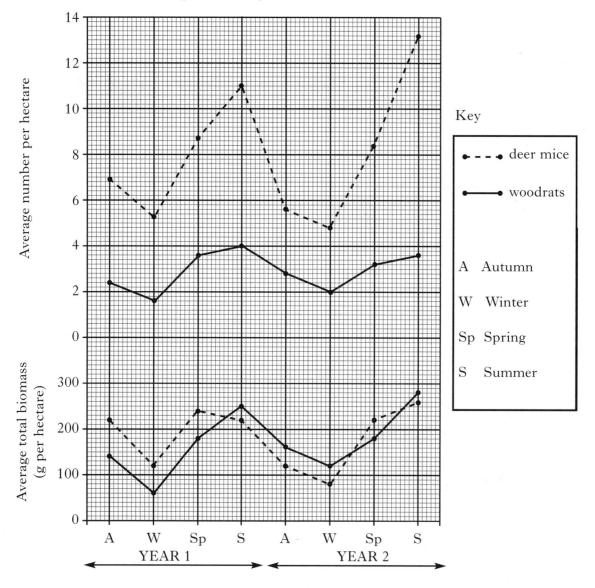

(a) (i) What percentage of the total number of prey eaten by owl pair A were deer mice?

Space for calculation

_____ %   1

5. **(a)** **(continued)**   *Marks*

(ii) Express as the simplest whole number ratio the numbers of deer mice, brush mice and rock squirrels eaten by owl pair B.

Space for calculation

deer mice   :   brush mice   :   rock squirrels

_____ : _____ : _____   **1**

(b) Use evidence from the table to identify the owl pair that foraged in a different habitat to the other two pairs of owls.

Justify your answer.

Pair _____

Justification _____

_____

_____   **1**

(c) (i) **Use values from the graph** to describe the change in average number of woodrats per hectare from spring of Year 1 until spring of Year 2.

_____

_____   **2**

(ii) Calculate the percentage decrease in the average total biomass of woodrats between summer of Year 1 and winter of Year 2.

Space for calculation

_____ %   **1**

(d) Calculate the average biomass of one deer mouse in summer of Year 1.

Space for calculation

_____ g   **1**

(e) The size of the territory of a pair of Mexican spotted owls is different in winter and summer. Give an explanation of this observation which can be supported by evidence from the graph.

_____

_____

_____   **1**

Marks

6. The diagram below shows a pair of homologous chromosomes in a mouse cell during meiosis. The positions of three genes R, S and T are also shown.

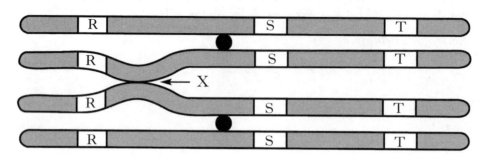

(a) Name an organ in mice where meiosis occurs.

_____ 1

(b) (i) Name point X where crossing over may occur.

_____ 1

(ii) Crossing over leads to recombination of genes.

Between which two genes in the diagram would the greatest frequency of recombination take place?

_____ and _____ 1

(iii) Crossing over is a source of genetic variation.

Name **one** other feature of meiosis which leads to genetic variation.

_____ 1

(c) A mouse egg contains 20 chromosomes.

State the number of chromosomes present in a mouse gamete mother cell.

_____ chromosomes 1

Marks

7. In Labrador dogs, the alleles **B** and **b** and alleles **E** and **e** are involved in the determination of coat colour.

   - Labradors with alleles **B** and **E** are always black.

   - Labradors with alleles **bb** and **E** are always chocolate coloured.

   - Labradors with alleles **ee** are always yellow.

   (*a*) A male black Labrador of genotype **BbEe** was crossed with a yellow female of the genotype **bbee**.

      (i) Complete the table below to show the genotypes of the gametes of the male.

Genotypes of male gametes			

       1

      (ii) Give the expected phenotype ratio of the offspring from this cross.

   Space for calculation

   _____ Black : _____ Chocolate :_____ Yellow   1

   (*b*) Give the genotype of a male Labrador which could be crossed with a female of genotype **bbee** to ensure that **all** the offspring produced would be chocolate coloured.

   Space for calculation

   Genotype _____   1

[Turn over

Marks

8. Cuticles are waxy layers on the surfaces of the leaves of many plant species.

The table below shows the average cuticle thickness of the leaves of five plant species and the rates of water loss through their cuticles at 20 °C with no air movement.

Species	Average cuticle thickness (micrometres)	Rate of water loss through cuticle (cubic micrometres per cm^2 per hour)
A	1·4	36·7
B	2·8	25·8
C	4·2	18·1
D	5·6	8·5
E	7·0	8·4

(*a*) (i) Describe the relationship between average cuticle thickness and rate of water loss through the cuticles in these plant species.

_____

_____

_____   **2**

(ii) Leaves lose most water through their open stomata.

Give the term used to describe the condition of the guard cells when stomata are open.

_____   **1**

(iii) State **two** changes to environmental conditions which could lead to an increase in water loss from leaves.

1 _____

2 _____   **1**

Marks

8. **(continued)**

(b) Plants which grow in extremely dry conditions have leaf adaptations which reduce water loss.

(i) Complete the table below to explain how each leaf adaptation reduces water loss.

Leaf adaptation	*Explanation of how the adaptation reduces water loss from leaves*
Presence of hairs on leaf surface	
Leaves small and few in number	

2

(ii) What term describes plants that have adaptations to reduce water loss?

_____ 1

[Turn over

Marks

9. (a) In an investigation into the effects of grazing, the total biomass of grass species and the diversity of all plant species in a field was monitored over a period of four years. The field was not grazed in years 1 and 2. Sheep grazed the field in years 3 and 4.

The results are shown on the graph below.

- - - - diversity   ———— biomass

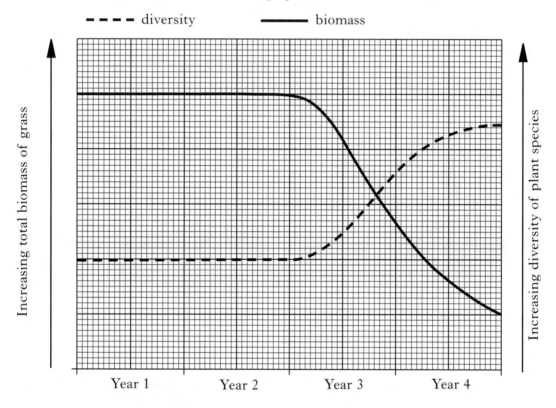

(i) Explain the effects of grazing by sheep on the total biomass of grass species and the diversity of plant species during year 3.

Total biomass of grass species.

_____ 1

Diversity of all plant species

_____

_____ 1

(ii) The number of sheep grazing the field was increased after year 4. Suggest how this would affect the diversity of plant species in the field.

Justify your answer.

Effect on diversity

_____

Justification

_____

_____ 1

Marks

9. **(continued)**

(*b*) The table below contains statements describing plant adaptations.

Complete the table by ticking (✓) the boxes to show the adaptations that help the plants tolerate the effects of grazing.

Plant adaptation	Tick (✓)
Dandelions have deep roots	
Wild roses have thorns	
Couch grass has underground stems	
Nettles have stings	
Tobacco plants produce nicotine	

2

[Turn over

Marks

10. Catechol oxidase is an enzyme found in apple tissue. It is involved in the reaction which produces the brown pigment that forms in cut or damaged apples.

$$\text{catechol} \atop \text{(colourless substance} \atop \text{in apple tissue)}} \quad \xrightarrow{\text{catechol oxidase}} \quad \text{brown pigments}$$

The effect of the concentration of lead ethanoate on this reaction was investigated.

$10\,g$ of apple tissue was cut up, added to $10\,cm^3$ of distilled water and then liquidised and filtered. This produced an extract containing both catechol and catechol oxidase.

Test tubes were set up as described in **Table 1** and kept at $20\,°C$ in a water bath.

Table 1

Tube	Contents of tubes
A	sample of extract + $1\,cm^3$ distilled water
B	sample of extract + $1\,cm^3$ 0.01% lead ethanoate solution
C	sample of extract + $1\,cm^3$ 0.1% lead ethanoate solution

Every 10 minutes, the tubes were placed in a colorimeter which measured how much brown pigment was present.

The more brown pigment present the higher the colorimeter reading.

The results are shown in **Table 2**.

Table 2

Time (minutes)	Colorimeter reading (units)		
	Tube A	Tube B	Tube C
	sample of extract + distilled water	sample of extract + 0·01% lead ethanoate	sample of extract + 0·1% lead ethanoate
0	1·6	1·8	1·6
10	7·0	5·0	2·0
20	9·0	6·0	2·2
30	9·6	6·4	2·4
40	10·0	7·0	2·4
50	10·0	7·6	2·4
60	10·0	7·6	2·4

(a)　(i)　Identify **two** variables not already mentioned that would have to be kept constant.

1 _____　1

2 _____　1

10. **(a)** **(continued)**

Marks

(ii) Describe how tube A acts as a control in this investigation.

_____

_____   1

(b) Explain why the initial colorimeter readings were not 0·0 units.

_____

_____   1

(c) The results for the extract with 0·1% lead ethanoate are shown in the graph below.

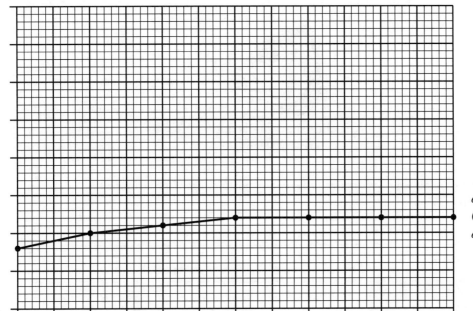

extract +
0·1% lead
ethanoate

Use information from **Table 2** to complete the graph by:

(i) adding the scale and label to each axis;   1

(ii) presenting the results for the extract + 0·01% lead ethanoate solution **and** labelling the line.   1

(Additional graph paper, if required, will be found on page 40.)

(d) State the effect of the concentration of lead ethanoate solution on the activity of catechol oxidase.

_____

_____   1

(e) The experiment was repeated with the 0·1% lead ethanoate solution at 60 °C. Predict the colorimeter reading at 10 minutes and justify your answer.

Prediction _____ units

Justification _____

_____   1

Marks

11. Many species of cichlid fish are found in Lake Malawi in Africa.

The diagram below shows the heads of three different cichlid fish and gives information on their feeding methods.

These species have evolved from a single species.

Sucks in microscopic
organisms from the water

Scrapes algae from the
surfaces of rocks

Crushes snail shells and
extracts flesh

(a) Describe how the information given about these fish illustrates adaptive radiation.

_____

_____

_____   2

(b) What evidence would confirm that the cichlids are different species?

_____

_____   1

(c) The evolution of these cichlid fish has involved geographical isolation.

(i) Name another type of isolating mechanism.

_____   1

(ii) State the importance of isolating mechanisms in the evolution of new species.

_____

_____   1

Marks

12. Diagram A shows a section through a woody stem. Diagram B shows a magnified view of the area indicated on the section.

Diagram A   Diagram B

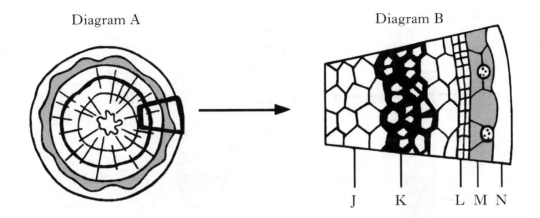

                                    J   K   L M N

(a) Which letter on diagram B shows the position of a lateral meristem?

Letter _____   1

(b) Name the tissue of which annual rings are composed.

_____   1

(c) In which season was the woody stem cut?

Explain your choice.

Season _____   1

Explanation _____

_____

_____   1

[**Turn over**

Marks

13. The diagram below shows information relating to the Jacob–Monod hypothesis of the control of gene action in the bacterium *Escherichia coli*.

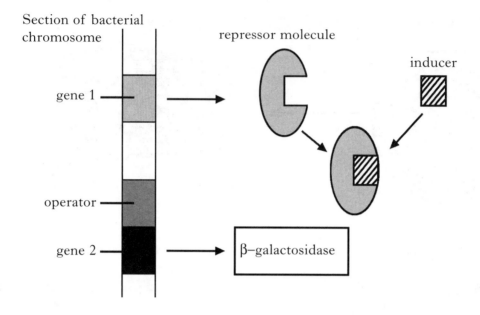

(a) Name gene 1.

_____   1

(b) Name the substance which acts as the inducer.

_____   1

(c) (i) Describe the sequence of events that occurs in the **absence** of the inducer.

_____

_____

_____

_____   2

(ii) Explain why it is important for *E. coli* to control gene action.

_____

_____   1

Marks

14. Environmental factors influence growth and development in animals.

(*a*) (i) Explain the importance of iron in the growth and development of humans.

_____

_____ **1**

(ii) Describe the effects of nicotine on growth and development of a human fetus.

_____

_____ **1**

(*b*) Breeding behaviour in red deer starts in autumn.

(i) Describe the environmental influence that triggers the start of breeding at this time of year.

_____

_____ **1**

(ii) Suggest an advantage to red deer of starting to breed at this time of year.

_____

_____ **1**

[Turn over

Marks

15. The diagram below shows the plant communities that have developed around a fresh water loch.

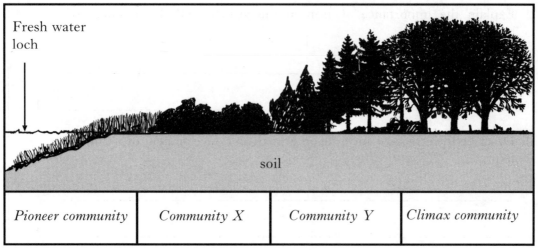

Fresh water loch

soil

| Pioneer community | Community X | Community Y | Climax community |

Increasing age of communities ⟶

(*a*) What term describes the process of gradual formation of a climax community?

_____   1

(*b*) Suggest a modification that community X may make to its habitat which allows colonisation by community Y.

_____

_____   1

(*c*) **Underline** one alternative in each pair to make the sentences correct.

The complexity of the food web in the climax community will be

$\left\{ \begin{array}{l} \text{greater than} \\ \text{less than} \end{array} \right\}$ that in the pioneer community.

Greater species diversity will exist in $\left\{ \begin{array}{l} \text{community X} \\ \text{community Y} \end{array} \right\}$.   1

SECTION C

Marks

Both questions in this section should be attempted.

Note that each question contains a choice.

Questions 1 and 2 should be attempted on the blank pages which follow.

Supplementary sheets, if required, may be obtained from the invigilator.

All answers must be written clearly and legibly in ink.

Labelled diagrams may be used where appropriate.

1. Answer **either** A **or** B.

    A. Write notes on:

       (i)   structure of the plasma membrane;   **4**

      (ii)   function of the plasma membrane in active transport;   **3**

     (iii)   structure and function of the cell wall.   **3**

          (10)

    OR

    B. Write notes on :

       (i)   the structure of DNA;   **6**

      (ii)   DNA replication and its importance.   **4**

          (10)

In question 2, ONE mark is available for coherence and ONE mark is available for relevance.

2. Answer **either** A **or** B.

    A. Give an account of the importance of nitrogen, phosphorus and magnesium in plant growth and describe the symptoms of their deficiency.   **(10)**

    OR

    B. Give an account of how animal populations are regulated by density-dependent and by density-independent factors.   **(10)**

[*END OF QUESTION PAPER*]

[Turn over

SPACE FOR ANSWERS

Page thirty-four

SPACE FOR ANSWERS

SPACE FOR ANSWERS

SPACE FOR ANSWERS

SPACE FOR ANSWERS

SPACE FOR ANSWERS

Page thirty-nine **[Turn over**

SPACE FOR ANSWERS

ADDITIONAL GRAPH PAPER FOR QUESTION 10(*c*)

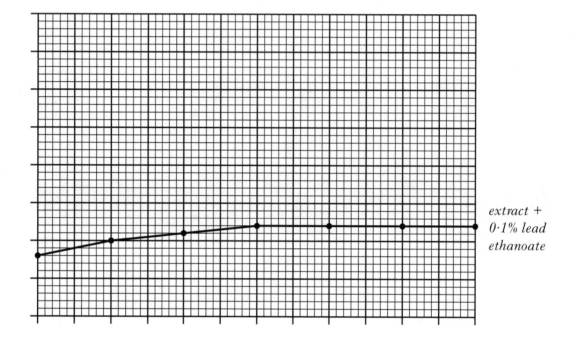

*extract +
0·1% lead
ethanoate*

[BLANK PAGE]

FOR OFFICIAL USE

Total for
Sections
B and C

X007/301

NATIONAL
QUALIFICATIONS
2010

THURSDAY, 27 MAY
1.00 PM – 3.30 PM

BIOLOGY
HIGHER

Fill in these boxes and read what is printed below.

Full name of centre

Town

Forename(s)

Surname

Date of birth

Day   Month   Year   Scottish candidate number   Number of seat

SECTION A—Questions 1–30 (30 marks)

Instructions for completion of Section A are given on page two.

For this section of the examination you must use an **HB pencil**.

SECTIONS B AND C (100 marks)

1   (a)   All questions should be attempted.

(b)   It should be noted that in **Section C** questions 1 and 2 each contain a choice.

2   The questions may be answered in any order but all answers are to be written in the spaces provided in this answer book, **and must be written clearly and legibly in ink**.

3   Additional space for answers will be found at the end of the book. If further space is required, supplementary sheets may be obtained from the Invigilator and should be inserted inside the **front** cover of this book.

4   The numbers of questions must be clearly inserted with any answers written in the additional space.

5   Rough work, if any should be necessary, should be written in this book and then scored through when the fair copy has been written. If further space is required a supplementary sheet for rough work may be obtained from the Invigilator.

6   Before leaving the examination room you must give this book to the Invigilator. If you do not, you may lose all the marks for this paper.

Read carefully

1   Check that the answer sheet provided is for **Biology Higher (Section A)**.

2   For this section of the examination you must use an **HB pencil**, and where necessary, an eraser.

3   Check that the answer sheet you have been given has **your name**, **date of birth**, **SCN** (Scottish Candidate Number) and **Centre Name** printed on it.

Do not change any of these details.

4   If any of this information is wrong, tell the Invigilator immediately.

5   If this information is correct, **print** your name and seat number in the boxes provided.

6   The answer to each question is **either** A, B, C or D. Decide what your answer is, then, using your pencil, put a horizontal line in the space provided (see sample question below).

7   There is **only one correct** answer to each question.

8   Any rough working should be done on the question paper or the rough working sheet, **not** on your answer sheet.

9   At the end of the examination, put the **answer sheet for Section A inside the front cover of this answer book**.

Sample Question

The apparatus used to determine the energy stored in a foodstuff is a

A   calorimeter

B   respirometer

C   klinostat

D   gas burette.

The correct answer is **A**—calorimeter. The answer **A** has been clearly marked in **pencil** with a horizontal line (see below).

Changing an answer

If you decide to change your answer, carefully erase your first answer and using your pencil fill in the answer you want. The answer below has been changed to **D**.

SECTION A

All questions in this section should be attempted.

Answers should be given on the separate answer sheet provided.

1. The diagram below represents an osmosis experiment, using a model cell.

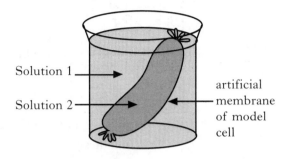

Which line of the table below shows a correct result for the solutions used in the experiment?

	Solution 1	Solution 2	Change of volume in model cell
A	water	5% sucrose	decrease
B	10% sucrose	water	increase
C	10% sucrose	5% sucrose	increase
D	10% sucrose	15% sucrose	increase

2. The cells of seaweed which actively absorb iodide ions from sea water would be expected to have large numbers of

   A   chloroplasts

   B   mitochondria

   C   ribosomes

   D   vacuoles.

3. An investigation was carried out into the uptake of sodium ions by animal cells. The graph below shows the rates of sodium ion uptake and breakdown of glucose at different concentrations of oxygen.

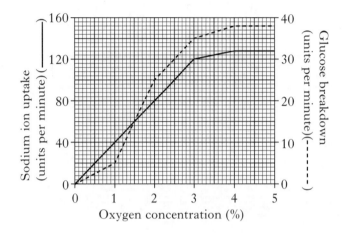

How many units of sodium ions are taken up over a 5 minute period when the concentration of oxygen in solution is 2%?

   A   80

   B   100

   C   400

   D   500

4. Which line in the table below correctly shows the two chemical reactions which occur in the grana of a chloroplast following the absorption of light energy by chlorophyll?

	Chemical reaction 1	Chemical reaction 2
A	ATP → ADP + Pi	water → hydrogen + oxygen
B	ADP + Pi → ATP	water → hydrogen + oxygen
C	ATP → ADP + Pi	hydrogen + oxygen → water
D	ADP + Pi → ATP	hydrogen + oxygen → water

5. Which line in the table below correctly shows the number of molecules of ATP used and produced when one molecule of glucose undergoes glycolysis?

	Number of molecules of ATP	
	Used	Produced
A	0	2
B	2	0
C	2	4
D	4	2

6. The graphs below show the results of an experiment into the effect of aerobic and anaerobic conditions on the uptake of calcium and magnesium ions by pond algae.

Uptake of calcium ions by pond algae

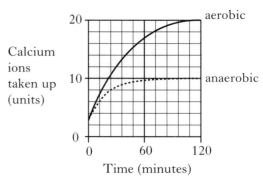

Uptake of magnesium ions by pond algae

Which of the following is a valid conclusion that can be drawn from the results?

A   At 120 minutes in aerobic conditions the uptake of calcium ions is greater than that of magnesium ions.

B   At 60 minutes in anaerobic conditions there was a greater uptake of calcium ions compared with magnesium ions.

C   Over the 120 minutes in aerobic conditions the average rate of uptake of calcium ions is greater than that of magnesium ions.

D   At 60 minutes in anaerobic conditions there was a greater uptake of magnesium ions compared with calcium ions.

7. The table below refers to processes in cellular respiration.

Process	Carbon dioxide produced	Water produced
X	no	no
Y	yes	no
Z	no	yes

Which line in the table below correctly identifies processes X, Y and Z?

	X	Y	Z
A	glycolysis	Krebs cycle	cytochrome system
B	Krebs cycle	glycolysis	cytochrome system
C	cytochrome system	Krebs cycle	glycolysis
D	glycolysis	cytochrome system	Krebs cycle

8. The diagram below represents the chemical structure of the protein ADH.

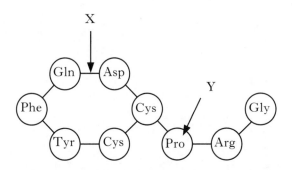

Which line in the table below identifies X and Y correctly?

	X	Y
A	hydrogen bond	base
B	hydrogen bond	amino acid
C	peptide bond	base
D	peptide bond	amino acid

9. A fragment of DNA was found to have 120 guanine bases and 60 adenine bases. What is the total number of sugar molecules in this fragment?

A   60

B   90

C   180

D   360

10. Which of the following statements about viruses is true?

A   Viral protein directs the synthesis of new viruses.

B   New viruses are assembled outside the host cell.

C   Viral protein is injected into the host cell.

D   Viral DNA directs the synthesis of new viruses.

11. Which line in the table below correctly describes the cells produced by meiosis?

	Cells produced by meiosis	
	Chromosome complement	Genetic composition
A	haploid	all cells different
B	diploid	all cells identical
C	diploid	all cells different
D	haploid	all cells identical

[Turn over

12. In mice, coat length is determined by the dominant allele **L** for long coat and the recessive allele **l** for short coat.

Coat colour is determined by the dominant allele for brown colour **B** and recessive allele for white colour **b**.

The genes are not linked.

What proportion of the offspring produced from a cross between two mice heterozygous for coat length and colour would have short brown coats?

A   1 in 16

B   3 in 16

C   9 in 16

D   1 in 4

13. Cystic fibrosis is an inherited condition caused by a recessive allele. The diagram below shows a family tree with affected individuals.

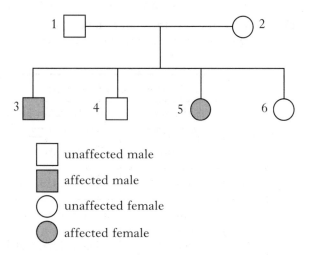

unaffected male

affected male

unaffected female

affected female

Which individuals in this family tree **must** be heterozygous for this condition?

A   3 and 5

B   4 and 6

C   1 and 2

D   2 and 6

14. In *Drosophila*, wings can be straight or curly and body colour can be black or grey.

Heterozygous flies with straight wings and black bodies were crossed with curly-winged and grey bodied flies.

The following results were obtained.

Number	797	806	85	89
Phenotype	straight wings and black bodies	curly wings and grey bodies	straight wings and grey bodies	curly wings and black bodies

These proportions of offspring suggest that

A   genes for body colour and wing shape are on separate chromosomes

B   crossing over has caused linked genes to separate

C   the genes show independent assortment

D   the genes must be carried on the sex chromosomes.

15. The diagram below represents the evolution of bread wheat. The diploid chromosome numbers of the species involved are given.

Triticum monococcum   X   Wild *Triticum* species
(2n = 14)   (2n = 14)

↓

Sterile hybrid 1

↓

Total non-disjunction

↓

Triticum turgidum   X   *Triticum*
(emmer wheat)   *tauschii*

↓

Sterile hybrid 2

↓

Total non-disjunction

↓

Triticum aestivum
(bread wheat)
(2n = 42)

Which line in the table below identifies correctly the diploid chromosome numbers of *Triticum turgidum* (emmer wheat) and *Triticum tauschii*?

	Triticum turgidum	*Triticum tauschii*
A	14	14
B	28	14
C	14	28
D	28	28

16. The flow chart below represents the programming of *E. coli* bacteria to produce human insulin.

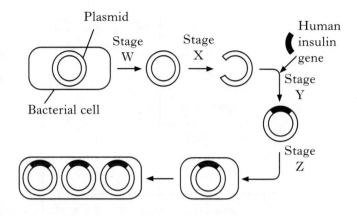

Which line in the table below identifies correctly the stages at which an endonuclease and a ligase are used?

	Endonuclease	*Ligase*
A	Stage X	Stage W
B	Stage Y	Stage Z
C	Stage X	Stage Y
D	Stage Y	Stage X

17. Which of the following statements could be **true** of cooperative hunting?

1 Individuals gain more energy than from hunting alone.

2 Both dominant and subordinate animals benefit.

3 Much larger prey may be killed than by hunting alone.

A   1 and 2 only

B   1 and 3 only

C   2 and 3 only

D   1, 2 and 3

[Turn over

18. The table below shows the mass of water gained and lost by a small mammal over a 24-hour period.

	Mass of water lost or gained (g)
Food	6
Metabolic water	54
Exhaled air	45
Urine	12
Faeces	3

What percentage of water gained comes from metabolic water?

A 9%

B 45%

C 54%

D 90%

19. The graph below shows the relationship between the ratio of body masses of two male fish and the average time they spend fighting for territory.

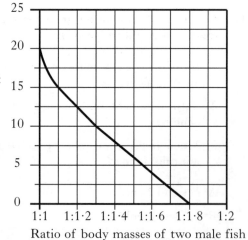

For how long will a fight between two fish, weighing 6 g and 9 g respectively, be expected to last?

A 6 minutes

B 10 minutes

C 15 minutes

D 17 minutes

20. Increased grazing by herbivores in a grassland habitat can result in an increase in the number of different plant species present in the habitat.

This is because

A some plants tolerate grazing because they have low meristems

B damage to dominant grasses by grazing allows the survival of other species

C grasses can regenerate quickly following damage by herbivores

D many grassland species produce toxins in response to grazing.

21. The diagram below shows a section of a woody twig.

Which is a region of summer wood?

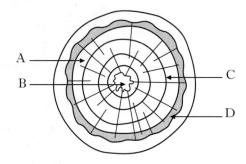

22. According to the Jacob-Monod hypothesis, a regulator gene is responsible for

A coding for the production of an inducer molecule

B switching on an operator

C coding for the production of a repressor molecule

D switching on a structural gene.

23. The graph below shows the effect of photoperiod on the onset of flowering in a species of plant.

% of plants starting to flower

Photoperiod (hours)

The graph shows that the plant is a

A long day species with a critical photoperiod of 8 hours

B long day species with a critical photoperiod of 14 hours

C short day species with a critical photoperiod of 8 hours

D short day species with a critical photoperiod of 14 hours.

24. The following list shows the effects of drugs on fetal development in humans.

1 Limb deformation

2 Overall reduction of growth

3 Slowing of mental development

Which line in the table below correctly matches alcohol, nicotine and thalidomide with their effects on fetal development?

	Alcohol	Nicotine	Thalidomide
A	2 only	2 and 3 only	1 and 3 only
B	3 only	2 and 3 only	1 only
C	2 and 3 only	2 only	1 and 3 only
D	2 and 3 only	2 and 3 only	1 only

25. Which line in the table below identifies correctly the hormones which stimulate the conversion of glucose and glycogen?

	glycogen → glucose	glucose → glycogen
A	glucagon and adrenalin	insulin
B	adrenalin	glucagon and insulin
C	insulin	adrenalin and glucagon
D	glucagon and insulin	adrenalin

26. Drinking a large volume of water will lead to

A increased production of ADH and kidney tubules becoming more permeable to water

B decreased production of ADH and kidney tubules becoming less permeable to water

C increased production of ADH and kidney tubules becoming less permeable to water

D decreased production of ADH and kidney tubules becoming more permeable to water.

[Turn over

27. The graph below shows how the concentration of insulin in the blood varies with the concentration of glucose in the blood.

What total mass of glucose would be present at an insulin concentration of 10 units/cm^3, in an individual with 5 litres of blood?

A   60 mg

B   300 mg

C   3000 mg

D   6000 mg

28. The graph below shows the annual variation in the biomass and population density of *Corophium*, a small burrowing invertebrate found in the mud of most Scottish estuaries.

Key

☐ = Biomass

■ = Population density

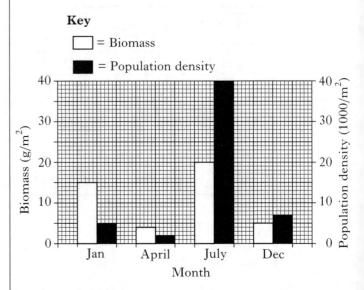

During which month do individual *Corophium* have the greatest average mass?

A   January

B   April

C   July

D   December

29. The graph below shows the effect of air temperature on the metabolic rate of two different animals.

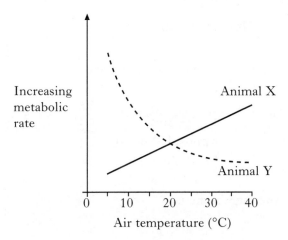

Which line in the table below identifies correctly the temperatures at which oxygen consumption will be greatest in the tissues of each animal?

	Animal X	Animal Y
A	20 °C	20 °C
B	40 °C	40 °C
C	40 °C	5 °C
D	5 °C	40 °C

30. Which of the following comparisons of early and late succession in plant communities in their habitat is correct?

	Early succession	Late succession
A	low biomass	high biomass
B	complex food webs	simple food webs
C	soil is deep	soil is shallow
D	high species diversity	low species diversity

Candidates are reminded that the answer sheet MUST be returned INSIDE the front cover of this answer book.

[Turn over

DO NOT
WRITE IN
THIS
MARGIN

Marks

SECTION B

All questions in this section should be attempted.

All answers must be written clearly and legibly in ink.

1. (*a*) The following sentences give information about the plasma membrane of beetroot cells.

   <u>**Underline**</u> one alternative in each pair to make the sentences correct.

   The plasma membrane contains $\left\{ \begin{array}{c} \text{cellulose} \\ \text{protein} \end{array} \right\}$ and $\left\{ \begin{array}{c} \text{phospholipids} \\ \text{carbohydrate} \end{array} \right\}$

   and has a $\left\{ \begin{array}{c} \text{fibrous} \\ \text{porous} \end{array} \right\}$ nature. As a result, the membrane is

   $\left\{ \begin{array}{c} \text{fully} \\ \text{selectively} \end{array} \right\}$ permeable.   2

   (*b*) Cyanide is a poison that inhibits enzymes involved in aerobic respiration.

   The graph below shows how cyanide concentration affects the uptake of chloride ions by beetroot cells.

   The rates of chloride ion uptake are given as percentages of those obtained in a control experiment with no cyanide.

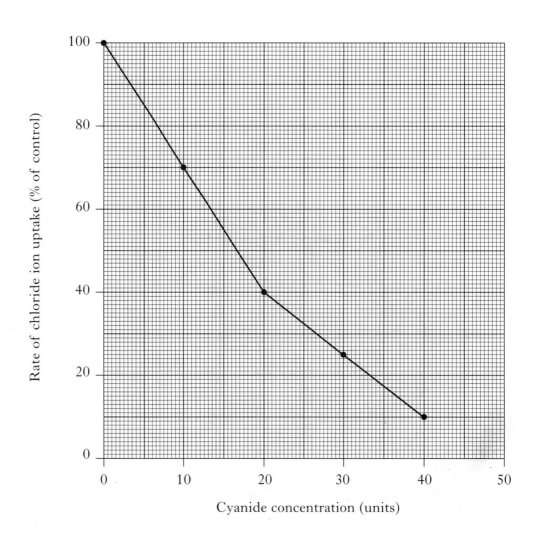

Marks

1. **(b)** **(continued)**

(i) Predict the cyanide concentration at which chloride ion uptake would stop.

_____ units   1

(ii) The rate of chloride ion uptake by beetroot at 30 units of cyanide was 200 μg per hour.

Calculate the rate of uptake in the control experiment.

Space for calculation

_____ μg per hour   1

(iii) The uptake of chloride ions occurs by active transport.

Explain how the information given supports this statement.

_____

_____

_____

_____   2

[Turn over

Marks

2. (a) State the **exact** location of photosynthetic pigments in plant leaf cells.

_____ 1

(b) The table below shows the mass of photosynthetic pigments in the leaves of two plant species.

Photosynthetic pigment	Mass of photosynthetic pigment in the leaves (μg per cm^3 of leaf)	
	Species A	Species B
chlorophyll a	0·92	0·93
chlorophyll b	0·34	0·35
carotene	0·32	0·65
xanthophyll	0·28	0·55

Which species is best adapted to grow in the shade of taller plants?

Explain your choice.

Species _____

Explanation _____

_____

_____ 1

Marks

2. (continued)

(c) The diagram below shows some events in the carbon fixation stage (Calvin cycle) of photosynthesis in a plant kept in bright light.

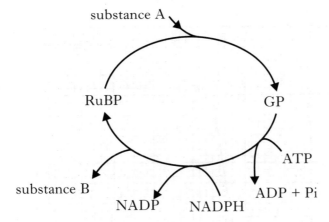

(i) Name substances A and B.

A _____

B _____   2

(ii) NADP carries hydrogen to the carbon fixation stage.

Describe the role of hydrogen in the carbon fixation stage.

_____

_____   1

(iii) Complete the table below to show the number of carbon atoms in one molecule of each compound.

Compound	Number of carbon atoms per molecule
RuBP	
GP	

1

(iv) Predict what would happen to the concentrations of RuBP and GP in leaf cells if the plant was moved from bright light into dark conditions.

Explain your answer.

RuBP _____

GP _____   1

Explanation _____

_____   1

Marks

3. In an investigation, yeast was grown in a glucose solution for 160 minutes in a sterilised fermenter. Temperature was kept constant and anaerobic conditions were maintained. The graph below shows the changes in concentration of ethanol in the fermenter during the period.

Time (minutes)

(a) (i) Calculate the increase in concentration of ethanol between 60 and 140 minutes.

Space for calculation

_____ grams per litre   **1**

(ii) Calculate the average increase in ethanol concentration per minute during the first 40 minutes.

Space for calculation

_____ grams per litre per minute   **1**

(b) (i) At point A on the graph, the ethanol concentration stopped increasing when air temporarily leaked into the fermenter.

Explain this result.

_____

_____   **2**

(ii) Assuming no further air leaks, explain why the ethanol concentration stopped increasing at point B.

_____

_____   **1**

Marks

4. (*a*) The diagram below shows part of a DNA molecule during replication.

Key to bases

A — adenine
G — guanine
T — thymine
C — cytosine

(i) Identify parts X and Y.

X_____

Y_____   1

(ii) Name bases 1 and 2.

1 _____

2 _____   1

(iii) Name **two** substances, not shown on the diagram, which are necessary for DNA replication.

1 _____

2 _____   2

(iv) Name a cellular process for which DNA replication is essential.

_____   1

(*b*) DNA is also involved in protein synthesis.

During protein synthesis, tRNA molecules with the anticodon UAG attach to the amino acid isoleucine.

Identify the DNA base triplet which codes for isoleucine.

_____   1

Marks

5. (a) Tuberculosis is a disease caused by the bacterium *Mycobacterium tuberculosis*.

   When the tuberculosis bacterium enters the human body it stimulates the production of antibodies.

   (i) Name the type of cells which produce antibodies.

   _____   1

   (ii) What term is given to any substance that stimulates antibody production?

   _____   1

   (b) Leaf rust is a fungus which grows when its spores land on leaves. The fungus spreads over leaf surfaces causing damage.

   Single leaves from four different species of cottonwood tree were sprayed with identical volumes of a suspension of rust fungus spores. After 3 days the percentage of leaf area with fungal growth was measured.

   The tannin content in these leaves was also measured.

   The results are shown in the table below.

Cottonwood species	Percentage leaf area with fungal growth after 3 days	Tannin content in leaves (mg per g of leaf dry mass)
Black	2·4	40·6
Eastern	11·4	3·9
Narrow-leafed	4·3	11·7
Swamp	3·2	15·6

   (i) Express as the simplest whole number ratio, the tannin content in the leaves of the eastern cottonwood, narrow-leafed cottonwood and swamp cottonwood.

   Space for calculation

   _____ : _____ : _____   1
   eastern   narrow-leafed   swamp

   (ii) Which species of cottonwood appears most resistant to attack by leaf rust fungus?

   _____   1

Marks

5. **(b)** **continued**

(iii) What evidence is there that tannins give protection against leaf rust fungus?

_____

_____

_____ **1**

(iv) Why was the tannin content of the leaves measured in mg per g of leaf dry mass and not fresh mass?

_____

_____ **1**

[Turn over

DO NOT
WRITE I
THIS
MARGI

Marks

6. Honey bees are social insects. They forage for food at various distances from their hive. When a bee finds a food source, it returns to the hive and communicates the location of the food to other bees using body movements called waggle dances. These are performed several times with short intervals between them.

In an investigation, bees were fitted with radio tracking devices which allowed the distances they travelled from the hive to be measured. The waggle dances performed by each returning bee were studied. The average time taken for its waggle dance was recorded and the number of times it was performed in 15 seconds was counted.

The results are shown in the graph below.

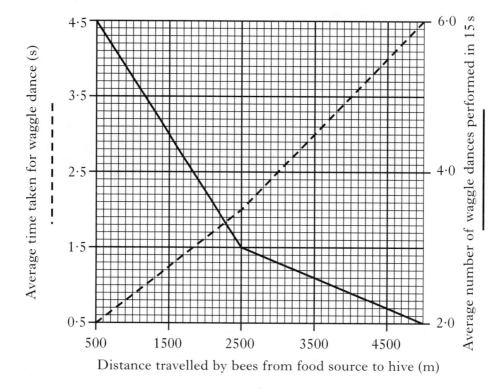

(a) (i) **Use values from the graph** to describe the relationship between the distance travelled by a bee from the food source and the number of waggle dances performed in 15 s.

_____

_____

_____   2

(ii) State the average time taken for a waggle dance when the distance travelled by a bee from the food source is 1500 m.

_____ s   1

Marks

6. **(*a*)** **(continued)**

(iii) Calculate the percentage increase in the average time taken for a waggle dance when the distance from the food source to the hive increases from 500 to 3500 metres.

Space for calculation

_____%   **1**

(iv) Predict the total time a bee would spend in the waggle dances in a 15 s period when the food source is 2500 m away from the hive.

_____ s   **1**

(*b*) In another investigation, the waggle dances of six bees from another hive were observed.

The results are shown in the table below.

BEE	*Number of times waggle dance was performed in 15 s*
1	2·65
2	2·20
3	2·30
4	2·55
5	2·70
6	2·60
Average	

(i) Complete the table by calculating the average number of times the waggle dance was performed in 15 s.

Space for calculation

1

(ii) Using information from the table and the graph, predict the distance that was travelled by bee 6 to its food source.

_____ m   **1**

(*c*) (i) Apart from its distance from the hive, what other information about food sources would be useful to the bees?

_____   **1**

(ii) In terms of the economics of foraging, explain the advantage of waggle dances to bees.

_____

_____   **1**

Marks

7. The diagram below shows a pair of homologous chromosomes during meiosis. P and Q show points where crossing over **may** occur. The other letters show the positions of the alleles of four genes.

(a) What evidence confirms that these chromosomes are homologous?

_____

_____ 1

(b) (i) What name is given to points P and Q?

_____ 1

(ii) State the importance of crossing over in meiosis.

_____

_____ 1

Marks

7.   **(continued)**

(c)   (i)   In the table below, tick (✓) the boxes to identify which combination of alleles would result from crossing over at point P only or crossing over at both points P and Q on the diagram.

Combination of alleles	Crossing over at	
	point P only	*both points P and Q*
Abcd		
aBCD		
AbcD		
aBCd		

1

(ii)   Give **one** possible sequence of alleles which could be found in a recombinant gamete formed if crossing over occurred at point Q only.

_____

1

[Turn over

Marks

8. (*a*) A rare form of rickets in humans is caused by a sex-linked allele **R** which is **dominant** to the allele **r**.

   (i) Complete the table below by inserting **all** possible genotypes of the female phenotypes of this allele.

Phenotype	*Genotype(s)*
Affected female	
Unaffected female	
Affected male	$X^R Y$
Unaffected male	$X^r Y$

2

   (ii) An affected female, whose father was unaffected, and an unaffected male have a son.

   What is the percentage chance that their son will be unaffected?

   Space for working

   _____ % chance   1

   (iii) The occurrence of allele **R** is due to a mutation in which the DNA triplet CAG is altered to TAG.

   Name this type of gene mutation and describe its effect on the structure of the protein it codes for.

   Name _____   1

   Description _____

   _____   1

(*b*) Rickets can also result from a deficiency of vitamin D in the diet.

State the role of vitamin D in humans.

   _____

   _____   1

Marks

9. (*a*) The table below refers to environmental problems that salt water bony fish and desert rats have in osmoregulation and adaptations that these animals use to maintain their water balance.

Complete the table by giving an environmental problem faced by salt water bony fish and adding **one** adaptation to each empty box.

Animal	Environmental problem	Adaptations for maintaining water balance	
		behavioural	*physiological*
Salt water bony fish		drinks sea water	
Desert rat	little drinking water available		

2

(*b*) The diagram below shows a section through a floating leaf of a hydrophyte plant.

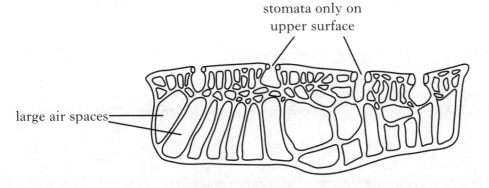

stomata only on
upper surface

large air spaces

Explain how the large air spaces allow this plant to survive in its environment.

_____

_____

_____

2

Marks

10.   The Jacob-Monod hypothesis describes lactose metabolism in the bacterium *Escherichia coli*. Lactose acts as an inducer of the enzyme β-galactosidase in the bacterium. This enzyme breaks down lactose as shown.

$$\text{lactose} \xrightarrow{\quad\text{β-galactosidase}\quad} \text{glucose + galactose}$$

An investigation of this reaction in *E. coli* at 25 °C was carried out as described below.

*   100 cm³ of gel beads coated with *E. coli* were placed into each of seven identical funnels fitted with outlet taps.

*   100 cm³ of solution containing 2 grams of lactose was poured into each funnel.

*   At each time shown in the table, the solution from one of the funnels was collected.

*   The mass of lactose in each solution was measured.

100 cm³ of gel beads coated with *E. coli* + 100 cm³ of lactose solution

funnel

outlet tap

beaker to collect solution

The results are shown in the table below.

Funnel	Time (minutes)	Mass of lactose in the solution collected (g)
1	0	2·00
2	10	2·00
3	20	1·48
4	30	0·92
5	40	0·40
6	50	0·12
7	60	0·04

(a)   (i)   Identify **one** variable, not already mentioned, that should have been controlled to ensure that the experimental procedure was valid.

_____   1

(ii)   A control experiment would be needed for each funnel.

Describe such a control and explain its purpose in the investigation.

Description _____

_____

Purpose_____

_____   2

Marks

10. **(continued)**

(b) On the grid provided below, draw a line graph to show the mass of lactose in the solution collected against time.

Use an appropriate scale to fill most of the grid.

(Additional graph paper, if required, will be found on *Page thirty-six.*)

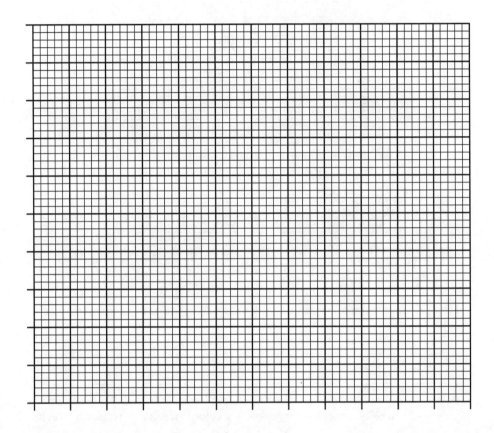

2

(c) Calculate the average mass of lactose broken down per minute in funnel 5.

Space for calculation

_____ g per minute 1

(d) Use the information given to explain why *E. coli* had not broken down any lactose in the first 10 minutes.

_____

_____

_____ 2

(e) State **one** advantage to *E. coli* of controlling lactose metabolism as described by the Jacob-Monod hypothesis.

_____ 1

Marks

11. (*a*) The graph below shows the change in the dry mass of an annual plant as it grows from a seed over an eight week period.

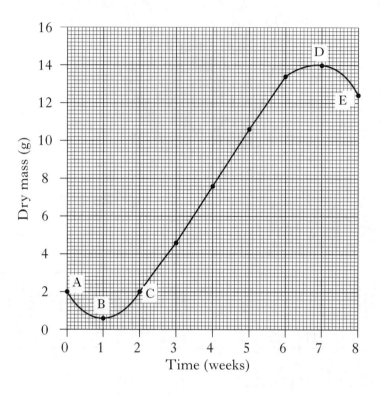

(i) Tick (✓) **two** boxes to identify periods when the rate of growth was the same.

☐ 0–1 weeks ☐ 1–2 weeks ☐ 2–3 weeks ☐ 3–4 weeks ☐ 4–5 weeks ☐ 5–6 weeks ☐ 6–7 weeks ☐ 7–8 weeks

1

(ii) Which letter indicates the beginning of germination?

Letter _____

1

(iii) Which process accounts for the rise in dry mass between B and C?

_____

1

(iv) Suggest a reason for the decrease in dry mass between D and E.

_____

1

(*b*) Apart from the increase in mass, state **one** other way in which the growth of an annual plant could be measured.

_____

1

(*c*) Name the region of a shoot or root tip of an annual plant in which cell division occurs.

_____

1

Marks

12. Phenylalanine and tyrosine are amino acids produced from the digestion of protein in the human diet. Once absorbed, they are involved in the metabolic pathway shown below.

The condition phenylketonuria (PKU) can be caused by the absence of enzyme 1.

(a) Describe what leads to the absence of enzyme 1 in this condition.

_____

_____   1

(b) Explain why individuals with PKU still develop some pigment in their skin.

_____

_____   1

(c) State the role of thyroxine in the human body.

_____

_____   1

[Turn over

Marks

13. The diagrams show three barley seedlings which were grown in culture solutions. Solution A had all elements required for plant growth. Solutions B and C were each missing in one element required for normal plant growth. The seedlings were kept under a lamp which provided constant bright light conditions.

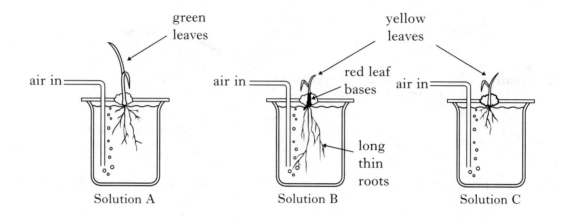

(a) Complete the table below by naming the element that was missing from culture solutions B and C and by giving a role for the element missing from solution B.

Solution	Element missing from solution	Role of element in plants
B		
C		component of chlorophyll

2

(b) In a further experiment, the seedling in solution A was grown in complete darkness for a week.

Give the term which would describe the seedling after this period and describe how the treatment would have affected its appearance.

Term _____   1

Description _____

_____   1

Marks

14. (*a*) The Colorado beetle is a pest of potato crops. In an investigation, the population of beetles in a $2000\,m^2$ potato field was estimated as described below.

A sample of the beetles from the field was collected and counted.

Each beetle was marked with a spot of paint then released back into the field.

Three days later a second sample of beetles was collected and counted.

The number of marked beetles in this second sample was noted.

The results are shown in the table below.

Number of beetles that were marked and released	*Number of beetles in second sample*	*Number of marked beetles in second sample*
500	450	5

The population of beetles can be estimated using the following formula.

$$\text{Population} = \frac{\text{number of beetles marked and released} \times \text{number of beetles in second sample}}{\text{number of marked beetles in second sample}}$$

(i) Calculate the **population density** of beetles in the field.

Space for calculation

_____ beetles per m^2 **1**

(ii) The beetle population is affected by both density-dependent and density-independent factors.

Name a density-dependent and a density-independent factor that could affect the population of beetles in the field.

Density-dependent factor _____

Density-independent factor _____   **1**

(*b*) A population of a species may be monitored to gain data for use in pest control.

State **two** further reasons why a wild population may be monitored.

1 _____

2 _____   **1**

[Turn over for Section C on *Page thirty-two*

Marks

SECTION C

Both questions in this section should be attempted.

Note that each question contains a choice.

Questions 1 and 2 should be attempted on the blank pages which follow.

Supplementary sheets, if required, may be obtained from the Invigilator.

All answers must be written clearly and legibly in ink.

Labelled diagrams may be used where appropriate.

1. Answer **either** A **or** B.

    A. Write notes on plant growth and development under the following headings:

        (i)   the effects of indole acetic acid (IAA);   **6**

        (ii) the role of gibberellic acid (GA) in the germination of barley grains.   **4**

                                                                                 (10)

    OR

    B. Write notes on the following :

        (i)   endotherms and ectotherms;   **2**

        (ii) temperature regulation in mammals.   **8**

                                                                                 (10)

In question 2, ONE mark is available for coherence and ONE mark is available for relevance.

2. Answer **either** A **or** B.

    A. Give an account of the importance of isolating mechanisms, mutations and natural selection in the evolution of new species.   **(10)**

    OR

    B. Give an account of the transpiration stream and its importance to plants.   **(10)**

[END OF QUESTION PAPER]

[BLANK PAGE]

FOR OFFICIAL USE

Total for
Sections
B and C

X007/301

NATIONAL
QUALIFICATIONS
2011

WEDNESDAY, 1 JUNE
1.00 PM – 3.30 PM

BIOLOGY
HIGHER

Fill in these boxes and read what is printed below.

Full name of centre

Town

Forename(s)

Surname

Date of birth

Day   Month   Year   Scottish candidate number   Number of seat

SECTION A—Questions 1–30 (30 marks)

Instructions for completion of Section A are given on page two.

For this section of the examination you must use an **HB pencil**.

SECTIONS B AND C (100 marks)

1 (a) All questions should be attempted.

   (b) It should be noted that in **Section C** questions 1 and 2 each contain a choice.

2 The questions may be answered in any order but all answers are to be written in the spaces provided in this answer book, **and must be written clearly and legibly in ink**.

3 Additional space for answers will be found at the end of the book. If further space is required, supplementary sheets may be obtained from the Invigilator and should be inserted inside the **front cover** of this book.

4 The numbers of questions must be clearly inserted with any answers written in the additional space.

5 Rough work, if any should be necessary, should be written in this book and then scored through when the fair copy has been written. If further space is required a supplementary sheet for rough work may be obtained from the Invigilator.

6 Before leaving the examination room you must give this book to the Invigilator. If you do not, you may lose all the marks for this paper.

Read carefully

1   Check that the answer sheet provided is for **Biology Higher (Section A)**.

2   For this section of the examination you must use an **HB pencil**, and where necessary, an eraser.

3   Check that the answer sheet you have been given has **your name**, **date of birth**, **SCN** (Scottish Candidate Number) and **Centre Name** printed on it.

    Do not change any of these details.

4   If any of this information is wrong, tell the Invigilator immediately.

5   If this information is correct, **print** your name and seat number in the boxes provided.

6   The answer to each question is **either** A, B, C or D. Decide what your answer is, then, using your pencil, put a horizontal line in the space provided (see sample question below).

7   There is **only one correct** answer to each question.

8   Any rough working should be done on the question paper or the rough working sheet, **not** on your answer sheet.

9   At the end of the examination, put the **answer sheet for Section A inside the front cover of this answer book**.

Sample Question

The apparatus used to determine the energy stored in a foodstuff is a

A   calorimeter

B   respirometer

C   klinostat

D   gas burette.

The correct answer is **A**—calorimeter. The answer **A** has been clearly marked in **pencil** with a horizontal line (see below).

Changing an answer

If you decide to change your answer, carefully erase your first answer and using your pencil fill in the answer you want. The answer below has been changed to **D**.

SECTION A

All questions in this section should be attempted.

Answers should be given on the separate answer sheet provided.

1. Equal sized pieces of potato were weighed then placed in different concentrations of sucrose.

   After 24 hours the potato pieces were removed and reweighed.

   For each potato piece the initial mass divided by the final mass was calculated.

   Which graph correctly represents the change in initial mass divided by final mass which would be expected as the concentration of sucrose increases?

   A

   B

   C

   D
   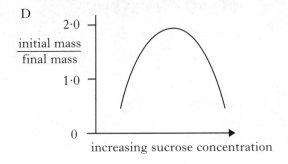

2. The graph below shows the rate of photosynthesis at two different levels of carbon dioxide concentration at 20 °C.

   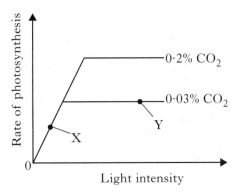

   From the evidence given, identify the factors most likely to be limiting the rate of photosynthesis at points X and Y on the graph.

	Point X	*Point* Y
A	Light intensity	CO_2 concentration
B	Temperature	Light intensity
C	CO_2 concentration	Temperature
D	Light intensity	Temperature

   [Turn over

3. The diagram below represents a summary of respiration in a mammalian muscle cell.

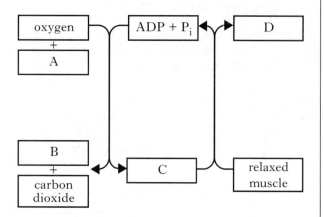

Which box represents ATP?

4. Which of the following produces water?

    A   Krebs cycle

    B   Glycolysis

    C   Photolysis

    D   Cytochrome system

5. The graph below shows changes which occur in the masses of protein, fat and carbohydrate in the body of a hibernating mammal during seven weeks without food.

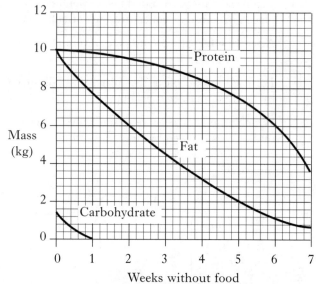

What percentage of the original mass of fat was used up between weeks 2 and 5?

    A   33%

    B   40%

    C   67%

    D   80%

6. Which of the following compounds are linked by peptide bonds to form more complex molecules?

    A   Bases

    B   Nucleic acids

    C   Nucleotides

    D   Amino acids

7. A DNA molecule consists of 4000 nucleotides, of which 20% contain the base adenine.

How many of the nucleotides in this DNA molecule will contain guanine?

    A   800

    B   1000

    C   1200

    D   1600

8. The diagram below shows parts of an animal cell.

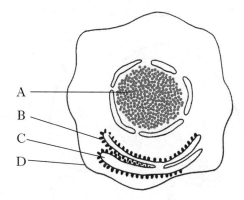

A
B
C
D

Where does synthesis of mRNA take place?

9. The function of tRNA in cell metabolism is to

A transport amino acids to be used in synthesis

B carry codons to the ribosomes

C synthesise proteins

D transcribe the DNA code.

10. Which of the following describes a cellular defence mechanism in plants?

A Growth of sharp spines

B Production of cellulose fibres

C Development of low meristems

D Secretion of sticky resin

11. Huntington's Disease is an inherited condition in humans caused by a dominant allele. A woman's father is heterozygous for the condition. Her mother is not affected by the condition.

What is the chance of the woman being affected by the condition?

A 1 in 1

B 1 in 2

C 1 in 3

D 1 in 4

12. In guinea pigs, brown hair **B** is dominant to white hair **b** and short hair **S** is dominant to long hair **s**.

A brown, long-haired male was crossed with a white, short-haired female. The F_1 phenotype ratio was

1 brown, short-haired:
1 white, short-haired:
1 brown, long-haired:
1 white, long-haired.

What were the genotypes of the parents?

	Male	*Female*
A	BbSs	BbSs
B	Bbss	bbSs
C	BBss	bbSS
D	bbSs	Bbss

13. The following cross was carried out using two true-breeding strains of the fruit fly, *Drosophila*.

Parents	straight wing black body	×	curly wing grey body

F_1 all straight wing black body

F_1 allowed to interbreed

F_2 3 straight wing black body : 1 curly wing grey body

The result would suggest that

A crossing over has occurred between the genes

B before isolation, F_1 females had mated with their own-type males

C non-disjunction of chromosomes in the sex cells has taken place

D these genes are linked.

[**Turn over**

14. The diagram below shows the chromosome complement of cells during the development of abnormal human sperm.

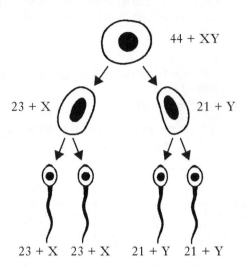

A sperm with chromosome complement 23 + X fertilises a normal haploid egg. What is the chromosome number and sex of the resulting zygote?

	Chromosome number	Sex of zygote
A	24	female
B	46	female
C	46	male
D	47	female

15. The diagram below represents the areas of interbreeding of 4 groups of birds, W, X, Y and Z.

Interbreeding takes place in the shaded areas.

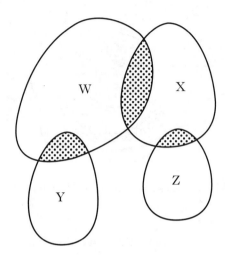

How many species are present?

A   1

B   2

C   3

D   4

16. In an investigation, peppered moths of both light and dark varieties were marked and released in three woodland areas. The numbers recaptured after 24 hours are shown in the table below.

Woodland area	Variety released	Number released	Number recaptured
1	Light	70	35
	Dark	30	15
2	Light	450	150
	Dark	300	150
3	Light	120	12
	Dark	220	22

The woodland areas were graded as polluted if the percentage of dark moths recaptured was greater than the percentage of light moths recaptured.

Which of the woodland areas were graded as polluted?

A 1 and 2 only

B 2 and 3 only

C 2 only

D 1 and 3 only

17. Apparatus X shown below is used in investigations into the rate of transpiration of a leafy twig.

Apparatus Y is a control used in such investigations.

The distance travelled by the air bubble in a given time measures the rate of transpiration in the leafy twig and the rate of evaporation from the porous pot.

Which line in the table below shows how the distance travelled by the air bubble changes when apparatus X and Y are moved from light to dark with all other variables kept constant?

	Distance travelled by air bubble (cm per minute)	
	Apparatus X	Apparatus Y
A	decreases	decreases
B	decreases	unchanged
C	increases	unchanged
D	increases	increases

[Turn over

18. The diagram below shows a cross section through the stem of a hydrophyte.

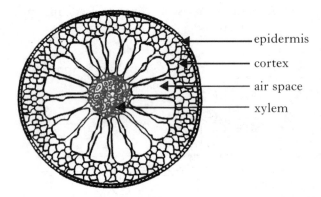

The arrangement of the xylem is of benefit to the plant because it

A   gives the stem flexibility in flowing water

B   allows uptake of water through the cortex

C   gives the stem increased support

D   allows transport of sugars to the roots.

19. The statements below relate to bird behaviour.

1   Blackbirds sing to mark their territory.

2   Arctic and common terns form large mixed breeding colonies.

3   Black grouse gather on open areas of short grass and males display to females.

4   Great skuas chase other seabirds and force them to drop their food.

Which of the above statements are related to intraspecific competition?

A   1 and 2 only

B   1 and 3 only

C   2 and 4 only

D   3 and 4 only

20. When the intensity of grazing by herbivores increases in a grassland ecosystem, diversity of plant species may increase as a result.

Which statement explains this observation?

A   Few herbivores are able to eat every plant species present.

B   Grazing stimulates growth in some plant species.

C   Vigorous plant species are eaten so less competitive species can now thrive.

D   Plant species with defences against herbivores are selected.

21. The diagram below shows a section through a woody twig.

Which label shows the position of a meristem?

22. In the condition phenylketonuria (PKU), the human body is unable to

A   synthesise phenylalanine from tyrosine

B   secrete phenylalanine from cells

C   absorb phenylalanine into the bloodstream

D   convert phenylalanine to tyrosine.

23. The diagram below shows an experiment to investigate the role of IAA in the growth of lateral buds.

Untreated shoot

Apical bud

Lateral bud

Apical bud removed and replaced by a jelly block

Jelly block

Apical bud removed and replaced by a jelly block containing IAA

Jelly block + IAA

Which line in the table correctly shows the expected growth of lateral buds in the experiment?

✓ = growth of lateral buds
✗ = no growth of lateral buds

	Untreated shoot	Apical bud removed and replaced by jelly block	Apical bud removed and replaced by a jelly block containing IAA
A	✗	✓	✗
B	✗	✗	✓
C	✓	✓	✗
D	✓	✗	✓

24. The table below shows the results of an experiment to investigate the effect of IAA on the development of roots from sections of pea stems.

Concentration of IAA (units)	Average number of roots per stem section
2	2·0
4	2·2
6	3·8
8	5·7
10	6·6

The greatest percentage increase in the average number of roots per stem section is caused by an increase in IAA concentration (units) from

A   2 to 4

B   4 to 6

C   6 to 8

D   8 to 10.

[Turn over

25. The graph below shows how female bone density changes with age.

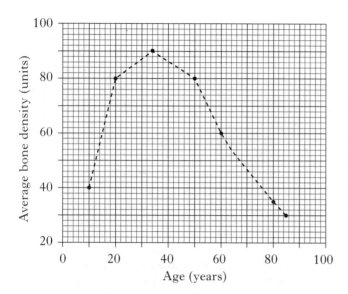

When a female's bone density falls to 60% of its maximum, there is an increased chance of bone breakage.

This occurs at

A   60 years

B   64 years

C   76 years

D   84 years.

26. The diagrams below represent the same barley seedling at 24 hours and 30 hours after germination.

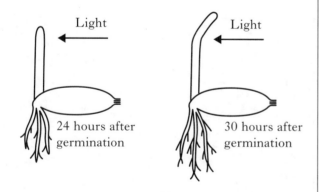

Which of the following is used to describe the growth movement observed?

A   Photoperiodism

B   Etiolation

C   Phototropism

D   Germination

27. Which line in the table below shows the critical factors for the onset of flowering in short and long day plants?

	Short day plants	Long day plants
A	length of light period	length of light period
B	length of dark period	length of dark period
C	length of light period	length of dark period
D	length of dark period	length of light period

28. An experiment was carried out to estimate the concentration of urea present in urine samples as shown in the diagram below.

The method involved adding tablets containing the enzyme urease to urine samples. Urease breaks down urea to produce ammonia.

The time taken for the ammonia produced to turn red litmus to blue was then measured.

Which **two** factors would have to be kept the same throughout the investigation?

A   Size of tablet and concentration of urea

B   Concentration of urea and time taken for red litmus to turn blue

C   Size of tablet and volume of urine used

D   Volume of urine used and time taken for red litmus to turn blue

29. Which line in the table below shows density-dependent and density-independent factors?

	Density-dependent	Density-independent
A	disease and competition	flood and drought
B	fire and flood	food supply and predation
C	food supply and disease	competition and predation
D	competition and fire	flood and drought

30. Which line in the table below identifies the characteristics of a climax community?

	Characteristic of climax community		
	Biomass	Species diversity	Food webs
A	low	high	simple
B	high	low	complex
C	low	low	simple
D	high	high	complex

Candidates are reminded that the answer sheet MUST be returned INSIDE the front cover of this answer book.

[Turn over

Marks

SECTION B

All questions in this section should be attempted.

All answers must be written clearly and legibly in ink.

1. The diagram below shows *Paramecium*, a unicellular organism found in fresh water.

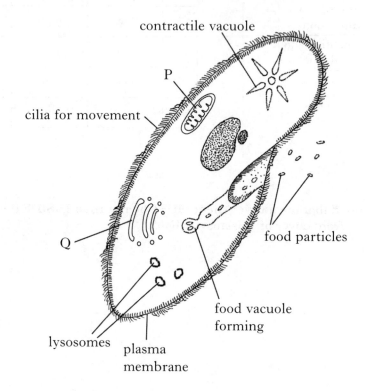

(*a*) Identify organelles P and Q.

P _____

Q _____   2

(*b*) (i) Name **two** chemical components of the plasma membrane.

1 _____

2 _____   1

(ii) Give a property of the plasma membrane which is related to its role in osmosis.

_____   1

Marks

1. **(continued)**

   (c) *Paramecium* has contractile vacuoles that fill with excess water which has entered the organism by osmosis. These vacuoles contract to remove this water from the organism.

   The rate of contraction of the vacuoles is affected by the concentration of the solution in which the *Paramecium* is found.

   In which solution would the highest rate of contraction of the vacuoles occur?

   Underline the correct answer.

   hypertonic   hypotonic   isotonic   1

   (d) *Paramecium* feeds on micro-organisms present in water.

   Use information from the diagram to describe how *Paramecium* obtains and digests food.

   _____

   _____

   _____   2

   [Turn over

Marks

2.   The diagram below shows an outline of respiration in yeast cells.

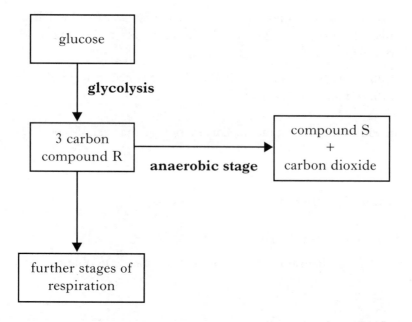

(a)   State the location of glycolysis in yeast cells.

_____   1

(b)   Name **one** substance, other than glucose, which must be present for glycolysis to occur.

_____   1

(c)   Name compounds R and S.

R _____   1

S _____   1

(d)   Explain why the further stages of respiration cannot occur in anaerobic conditions.

_____

_____

_____   1

Marks

3. The graph shows the rate of potassium ion uptake by human liver cells in different oxygen concentrations at 30 °C.

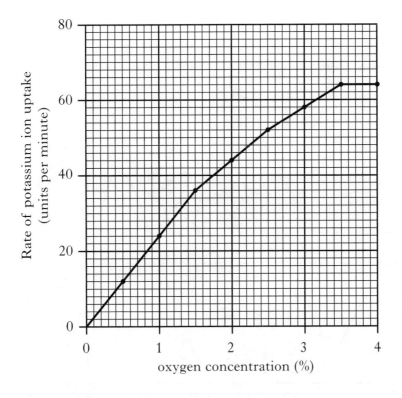

(a) When the oxygen concentration is 1%, how many units of potassium would a cell take up in one hour?

Space for calculation

_____ units per hour   **1**

(b) Suggest a reason why the graph levels off at oxygen concentrations above 3·5%.

_____

_____   **1**

(c) When the experiment was repeated at 20 °C, the potassium ion uptake decreased. Explain this observation.

_____

_____

_____

_____   **2**

Marks

4. (*a*) The diagram below shows the absorption spectrum of a single photosynthetic pigment from a plant and the rate of photosynthesis of the plant in different colours of light.

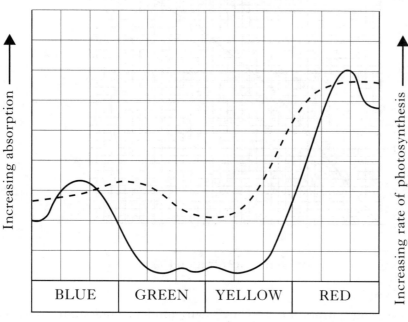

(i) Leaves of this plant contain more than one photosynthetic pigment.

Use evidence from the graph to justify this statement.

_____

_____

_____   1

(ii) Name a technique used to separate mixtures of photosynthetic pigments.

_____   1

Marks

4. (continued)

(b) *Spirogyra* is a photosynthetic green alga which grows as a long strand of cells. A strand of *Spirogyra* was placed into water containing aerobic bacteria. Different parts of the strand were exposed to different colours of light. After a period of time, the bacteria had moved into the positions shown in the diagram below.

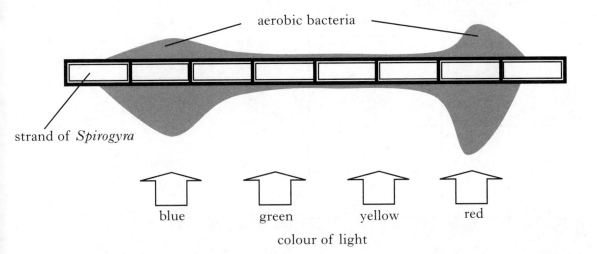

Explain the distribution of aerobic bacteria shown in the diagram.

_____

_____

_____

_____   2

[Turn over

Marks

5. (*a*) Eye colour in fruit flies is sex-linked.

Red eye colour **R** is dominant to white eye colour **r**.

A heterozygous red-eyed female fly was crossed with a white-eyed male.

(i) Complete the grid by adding the genotypes of

1 the male and female gametes;   **1**

2 the possible offspring.   **1**

	Female gametes	
Male gametes		

(ii) Tick (✓) the box(es) to show all the expected phenotypes of the offspring from this cross.

red-eyed female ☐   white-eyed female ☐

red-eyed male ☐   white-eyed male ☐   **1**

(iii) Explain why the actual phenotype **ratio** obtained from this cross could differ from the expected.

_____

_____   **1**

Marks

5. (continued)

(b) Genes K, L, M and N are located on the same chromosome in fruit flies.

The recombination frequencies of pairs of these genes are given in the table.

Genes	Recombination frequency (%)
K and L	18
N and L	25
M and N	17
L and M	8
K and N	7

Complete the diagram below to show the relative positions of genes L, M and N on the chromosome.

K

1

[Turn over

Marks

6. The compensation point is the light intensity at which a plant's carbon dioxide uptake by photosynthesis is equal to its carbon dioxide output from respiration.

In some plant species, compensation point can be reduced when the plant is moved from bright light to shaded conditions.

Graph 1 shows how the compensation points of three species of plant changed over a 25 day period after they were moved from bright light into shaded conditions.

Graph 1

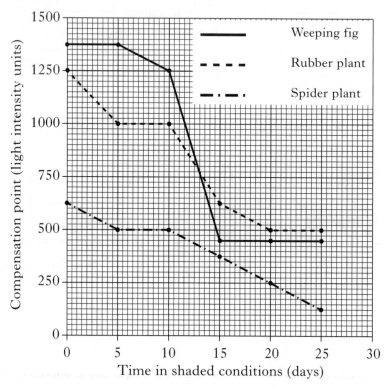

(a) (i) Use values from **Graph 1** to describe the changes in compensation point of the weeping fig over the 25 day period.

_____

_____

_____   2

(ii) Calculate the percentage decrease in compensation point of the rubber plant over the 25 day period.

Space for calculation

_____ %   1

(iii) Predict the compensation point of the spider plant at **28 days**.

_____ light intensity units   1

(iv) Use evidence from the graph to explain why the rubber plant could not grow successfully in a constant light intensity of 400 light intensity units.

_____

_____   2

Marks

6. **(continued)**

(b) After 10 days in shaded conditions, a plant of one species was placed into different light intensities and its carbon dioxide output and uptake were measured. This was repeated with another plant of the **same** species which had been in the shade for 20 days.

The results are shown in **Graph 2**.

Graph 2

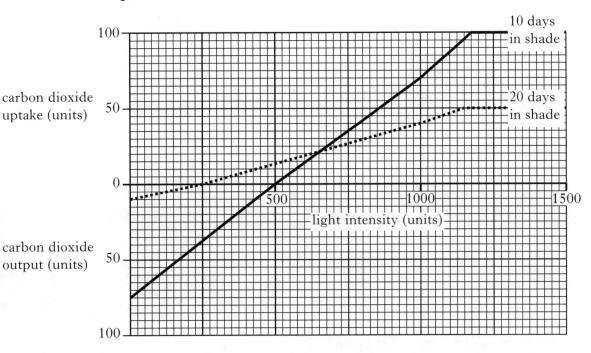

(i)   Use all the data to identify the plant species referred to in **Graph 2**.

Tick (✓) the correct box and give a reason for your choice.

weeping fig ☐   rubber plant ☐   spider plant ☐

Reason

_____

_____   1

(ii) From **Graph 2**, calculate how many times greater the carbon dioxide uptake of this plant was at 1000 units of light intensity after 10 days in shaded conditions compared with after 20 days in shaded conditions.

Space for calculation

_____ times   1

Marks

7. The table shows the base sequences of some mRNA codons and the amino acids for which they code.

mRNA codon			Amino acid
first base	*second base*	*third base*	
A	G	G	arginine
		C	serine
	A	A	lysine
		U	asparagine
	C	A	threonine
		C	threonine
	U	G	methionine
		U	isoleucine
C	G	A	arginine
		C	arginine
	A	G	glutamine
		U	histidine
	C	G	proline
		C	proline
	U	A	leucine
		U	leucine

(a) (i) State the mRNA codon for methionine.

_____   1

(ii) Use information from the table to identify the common feature of all mRNA codons which code for the amino acid arginine.

_____   1

(b) Complete the diagram below by naming the two amino acids corresponding to the bases on the strand of DNA shown.

Bases on strand of DNA

T A A G T C

Corresponding amino acids   1

Marks

8. Mutation rate can be increased artificially using chemical agents.

(a) Give **another** example of a mutagenic agent.

_____   1

(b) The table below shows the bases on part of a strand of DNA and the effects on the bases of four different gene mutations.

Original DNA strand	Gene mutation	Mutated DNA strands
ATCGCTA	1	ATCGGCTA
	2	ATCCTA
	3	ATCGCAA
	4	ATGCCTA

(i) Name the gene mutations which have caused the effects shown in the mutated strands.

gene mutation 1 _____

gene mutation 2 _____

gene mutation 3 _____

gene mutation 4 _____   2

(ii) Use numbers from the table to identify the **two** gene mutations that would result in the greatest changes to the structure of the protein coded for by the original DNA strand.

Explain how these mutations would lead to major changes in the structure of the protein.

Gene mutation numbers _____ and _____ .   1

Explanation _____

_____

_____   1

[Turn over

Marks

9. (a) The table shows behavioural adaptations of lions for obtaining food.

    (i) Complete the table below by explaining how each adaptation is beneficial for obtaining food.

Behavioural adaptation	Benefit for obtaining food
Cooperative hunting	
Territorial behaviour	

2

    (ii) These behavioural adaptations ensure that lions can forage economically.

    Explain what is meant by this statement in terms of energy gained and lost.

    _____

    _____

    _____   **1**

    (iii) Lions hunt wildebeest, which live in large herds.

    Explain how living in large herds benefits the wildebeest in terms of predation by lions.

    _____

    _____

    _____   **1**

Marks

9. **(continued)**

(*b*) If a snail is disturbed, it withdraws into its shell and re-emerges a few minutes later.

(i) Name the type of behaviour shown by the withdrawal response.

_____   1

(ii) What is the advantage to a snail of withdrawing into its shell?

_____

_____   1

[Turn over

10. Gibberellic acid (GA) is needed to break dormancy of rice grains allowing them to germinate.

An experiment was carried out to investigate the effects of GA on the germination of rice grains.

$30\,cm^3$ of different concentrations of GA solution was placed into separate beakers. 50 rice grains were added to each beaker. Each beaker was then covered with plastic film.

After 12 hours, the grains were removed from the solutions and evenly spaced in separate dishes on filter paper soaked with $20\,cm^3$ of water.

The dishes were covered and kept in the dark for 10 days and the number of germinated grains in each dish was counted.

A second batch of grains was treated in the same way but these were left in the GA solutions for 36 hours.

The results are shown in the table.

Concentration of GA solution (mg per litre)	Number of rice grains germinated	
	After 12 hours in GA solution	After 36 hours in GA solution
0	5	6
5	7	14
10	16	31
20	23	35
30	28	41
60	31	43

Marks

(a) Identify **one** variable, not already described, that should be kept constant.

_____   1

(b) (i) Explain how the solution with 0 mg per litre GA acts as a control in this experiment.

_____

_____   1

(ii) Suggest why some germination occurs in the control.

_____   1

(c) Identify a feature of the experimental procedure which ensured the reliability of the results.

_____   1

Marks

10. (continued)

(*d*) Predict how the concentration of GA in the beakers would have been affected if they had not been covered with plastic film.

Underline the correct answer and give a reason for your choice.

increased   decreased   stayed the same

Reason _____

_____ 1

(*e*) Calculate the difference in **percentage** germination between the grains kept in the 5 mg GA per litre solution for 12 hours and those kept in the 30 mg GA per litre solution for 12 hours.

Space for calculation

_____ % 1

(*f*) On the grid below, draw a line graph to show the number of grains germinated after 36 hours in the different concentration of GA solution.

(Additional graph paper, if required, will be found on *Page forty*.)

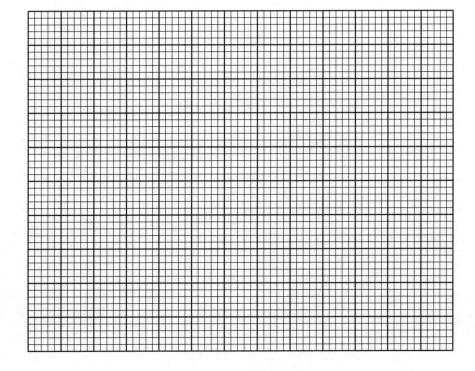

2

(*g*) Give **two** conclusions which can be drawn from the results in the **table**.

1 _____

2 _____ 2

Marks

10. (continued)

(*h*) GA induces the release of amylase in the germinating grains of plants such as rice and barley.

Name the site within the grains which produces amylase.

_____

1

Marks

11. The graph below shows how the body length of a locust changes over time.

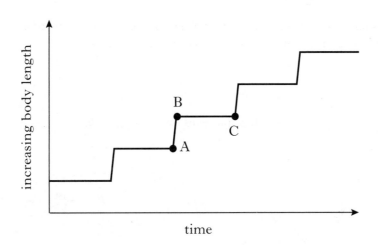

(a) Explain the growth pattern between points A and B and between points B and C shown on the graph.

A and B _____

_____ **1**

B and C _____

_____ **1**

(b) The diagram shows information about hormones involved in growth and development in humans.

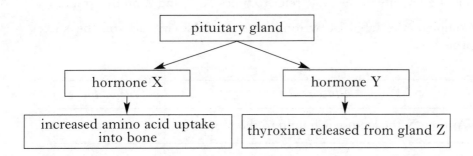

   (i) Name hormones X and Y.

   X _____ **1**

   Y _____ **1**

   (ii) Name gland Z.

   _____ **1**

   (iii) Describe the role of thyroxine in growth and development.

   _____

   _____ **1**

Marks

12. (*a*)   In the control of lactose metabolism in *Escherichia coli (E. coli)*, lactose acts as an inducer of the enzyme β-galactosidase.

The graph shows changes in concentrations of lactose and β-galactosidase after lactose was added to an *E. coli* culture growing in a container.

(i)   Describe how the graph supports the statement that β-galactosidase breaks down lactose.

_____

_____   1

(ii)   The statements in the table refer to times X, Y and Z on the graph.

Complete the table by writing **true** or **false** in each of the spaces provided.

Statement	True or False
At time X the lactose is bound to the repressor	
At time Y the lactose is bound to the operator	
At time Z the repressor is bound to the operator	

2

Marks

12. (continued)

(*b*) Complete the following sentences by <u>underlining</u> one of the alternatives in each pair.

Regeneration involves development of cells with specialised functions

from $\begin{Bmatrix} \text{differentiated} \\ \text{undifferentiated} \end{Bmatrix}$ cells through the switching on or off of

particular $\begin{Bmatrix} \text{hormones} \\ \text{genes} \end{Bmatrix}$.

Mammals have $\begin{Bmatrix} \text{limited} \\ \text{extensive} \end{Bmatrix}$ powers of regeneration.

2

[Turn over

Marks

13. The grid contains the names of substances that can influence growth and development in plants and animals.

A calcium	B nitrogen	C iron	D phosphorus
E vitamin D	F magnesium	G lead	H potassium

Use **letters from the grid** to answer the following questions.

Letters can be used once, more than once or not at all.

Each box should be completed using **one** letter only.

(a) Complete the table below.

Role in growth and development	Letter(s)
Important in membrane transport	
Present in chlorophyll	
Present in nucleic acids	
Needed for blood clotting	

4

(b) Complete the sentence.

Deficiency of ☐ leads to rickets as a result of

poor ☐ absorption in the intestine.

1

Marks

14. The list below shows conditions which must be maintained within tolerable limits in the human body.

List

A   blood glucose concentration
B   blood water concentration
C   body temperature

(a)   Use **all** the letters from the list to complete the table below to show where each condition is monitored.

Hypothalamus	*Pancreas*

1

(b)   The liver contains a reservoir of stored carbohydrate.

Name **two** hormones which can cause the breakdown of this carbohydrate to increase the concentration of glucose in the blood.

1 _____

2 _____   1

(c)   An increase in blood water concentration causes a reduction in the level of ADH in the bloodstream.

Describe the effect of this reduction on the kidney tubules.

_____

_____   1

(d)   (i)   When body temperature falls below normal, the blood vessels in the skin respond.

State how the blood vessels in the skin respond and explain how this helps return body temperature to normal.

Blood vessel response _____   1

Explanation _____

_____   1

(ii)   What term is used to describe animals which derive most of their body heat from their own metabolism?

_____   1

Marks

SECTION C

Both questions in this section should be attempted.

Note that each question contains a choice.

Questions 1 and 2 should be attempted on the blank pages which follow.

Supplementary sheets, if required, may be obtained from the Invigilator.

All answers must be written clearly and legibly in ink.

Labelled diagrams may be used where appropriate.

1. Answer **either** A **or** B.

   A. Write notes on maintaining a water balance under the following headings:

   (i)   osmoregulation in **salt water** bony fish;   **6**

   (ii) water conservation in the desert rat.   **4**

   (10)

   OR

   B. Write notes on meiosis under the following headings:

   (i)   first and second meiotic divisions;   **7**

   (ii) its role in the production of new phenotypes.   **3**

   (10)

In question 2, ONE mark is available for coherence and ONE mark is available for relevance.

2. Answer **either** A **or** B.

   A. Give an account of carbon fixation in photosynthesis and its importance to plants.   **(10)**

   OR

   B. Give an account of the production of new viruses after the invasion of cells and the role of lymphocytes in cellular defence.   **(10)**

[END OF QUESTION PAPER]

DO NOT
WRITE IN
THIS
MARGIN

SPACE FOR ANSWERS

SPACE FOR ANSWERS

SPACE FOR ANSWERS

Page thirty-seven   **[Turn over**

SPACE FOR ANSWERS

SPACE FOR ANSWERS

SPACE FOR ANSWERS

ADDITIONAL GRAPH PAPER FOR QUESTION 10(*f*)

HIGHER BIOLOGY
2007

Section A

1. A	2. D	3. B
4. D	5. D	6. D
7. D	8. C	9. A
10. A	11. B	12. B
13. A	14. A	15. C
16. A	17. D	18. C
19. C	20. C	21. B
22. A	23. D	24. C
25. B	26. C	27. B
28. C	29. D	30. B

Section B

1. (a) (i) Transmitted (through leaf) Transmission/transmittance
   (ii) Granum/grana (of chloroplast)

   (b) (i) Photolysis/photolytic splitting of water
   (ii) NADP

   (c) five
   carbon dioxide
   hydrogen
   three

2. (a) (i) 0·375 cm³
   (ii) Identical apparatus with no/dead worm or glass beads/plasticene (instead of worm)

   (b) 0·01

3. (a) (i) *0–3 hours*
   (Mass increases as) water enters/is gained/absorbed by osmosis.
   or Water diffuses into cell/enters from more dilute solution.
   or water enters/moves from High Water Concentration to Low Water Concentration.
   or water moves from higher water concentration/hypotonic (to hypertonic) region/solution.
   or Osmosis from HWC to LWC.
   or Water moves down a concentration gradient

   3–5 hours
   Cells/tissue/carrot turgid **or** tissue/cells isotonic with the solution.
   or (cell) wall stops more water entering/osmosis.
   or Wall has reached limits of elasticity

   (ii) (Temperature/heat) denatures/destroys/ damages protein in membrane.
   Making (the membrane) fully permeable/no longer selectively permeable.
   and allowing cell contents/water to escape/ leak out/be lost (giving a decrease in mass)

   (b) (i) Ion - chloride/chlorine
   Justification - concentration (of chloride) is equal/the same (inside and outside the organism)

(ii) Oxygen/aerobic conditions allows increased (aerobic) respiration that provides more ATP/energy, for more active transport (of potassium)

4. (a) (i) Transfer RNA/tRNA/TRNA
   (ii) Hydrogen (bond)

   (b) Codon

   (c) TTA
   (d) • Endoplasmic reticulum
   Carries/transports/ transfers/sends/passes (protein) to the Golgi (apparatus)
   • Golgi apparatus processes/packages/ modifies/adds carbohydrate to protein (for secretion).
   or packages secretion
   or produces vesicles containing protein

   (e)

Protein	Structure (Globular or Fribrous)	Function
Cellulase	**Globular**	Breaks down/ degrades/digests/ removes/destroys/gets rid of cell walls/cellulose **or** Makes protoplasts
Collagen	**Fibrous**	Structural protein in skin

5. (a) (i) Dominant/more competitive/faster growing/ prolific grasses/plants/species are eaten more/kept in check/prevented from taking over so other grasses/plants/species can grow
   (ii) At higher grazing intensity graph does not fall to zero/As grazing increases diversity never falls to zero.

   (b) • Low/basal/underground/close to ground meristems
   • Low/basal growing points
   • Underground stems/rhizomes
   • Deep root (systems) **or** roots lower in ground
   • Low apical meristems

6. (a) (i) June to October - increases from 3·6 g to 8·0 g/ by 4·4 g.
   October to November - remains constant/no change/levels off.
   November to December - decreases/reduces to 7·5 g/7.45 g/by 0·5 g.
   (ii) October to November
   (iii) 1:7
   (iv) 60%

   (b) Photosynthesis decreases/less starch made **and** starch used as an energy source/in respiration/as food **or** Starch converted to raffinose/used in growth/starch used in growth

   (c) (i) Raffinose concentration is less than the total sugar concentration
   (ii) Temperatures drop/winters are extremely cold/frost is likely **and** raffinose increases to prevent frost damage/ freezing of sap/needles
   or Higher concentration in winter/colder months helps to prevent frost damage (to needles)

7. (a) (i) Gamete mother (cells)
    (ii) Same genes/order of genes/gene sequence/ gene loci/position of genes
       or alleles/genes for same characteristics
       or chromosomes match each other gene for gene/same banding pattern
    (iii) (Partial) non-disjunction
    (iv) First meiotic division
       Justification - homologous chromosomes pair/are separating/fail to separate
       or homologous pairs form/separate/fail to separate.
       or does not involve separation of chromatids.
    (v) 2

(b) Insertion
Substitution

8. (a) (i) Barriers to gene exchange/gene flow/ interbreeding/spreading of mutations between groups/sub groups/populations
       or Splits the gene pool/creates two gene pools/prevents mixing of gene pool
    (ii) They have/share a common ancestor.
       Leaves selected for/adapted to/suited to/developed for different/their growing conditions/environment/niche/ climate.

(b) Spines/they/it give protection from/discourage/ reduce/stop grazing by herbivores/predators **and** reference to low growing

(c) • Wildlife/Nature reserves
   • captive breeding
   • breeding programmes
   • cell/seed/gene banks
   • hunting/fishing quotas
   • poaching bans
   • being made a protected species
   • breeding in zoos
   • only being allowed to hunt at certain times of the year

9. (a) (i) 2·5kg
    (ii) Increased/more growth hormone/GH (causes a growth spurt/rapid increase in growth) between 15 and 20 years/up to 20 years/through the teenage years. Decrease/less/no/cessation of growth hormone/GH (causes growth to cease) after 20 years/between 20 and 22 years.

(b) Thyroxine
Controls/regulates (the rate of) metabolism/ metabolic rate

10. (a) (i) *Any two from:*
   • temperature
   • type of soil
   • pH content of soil
   • mineral content of soil
   • fertility of soil
   • nutrients in soil
   • carbon dioxide conc./availability/level (in atmosphere)
   • distance/position/angle of spray from plant
    (ii) Use more pea plants at each concentration/mass of GA
       or
       Use more replicates at each conc/mass of GA

(b) (i)

Mass of GA applied (micrograms)

(ii) 370—380% increase

(c) Some spray may miss the plant **and** so less/ unknown/inaccurate mass of GA applied.

11. (a)

Statement	Lactose present	Lactose absent
Regulator gene produces the repressor molecule	T	T
Repressor molecule binds to inducer	T	F
Repressor molecule binds to operator	F	T

(b) (i) Phenylalanine - increases/builds up/rises/higher/more
       Tyrosine - decreases/falls/goes down/lower/less
    (ii) 1. (Mutation) changes order/sequence of bases/nucleotides (in a gene)
       or bases altered
       or Change to DNA code/sequence, mRNA code/sequence
       or Change to codon/codons/codon sequence
       2. (Leading to) change in (order/sequence of) amino acids
       3. Order/sequence of amino acids determines the (shape/function/structure of) protein/ enzyme

12. (a) Condition - continuous/uninterrupted/constant period of darkness must be 12 hours or more Justification - if dark period too short/less than 12 hours or interrupted then flowering does not occur

(b) Enables/allows sexual reproduction/cross pollination/interbreeding/cross-breeding
or Pollen able to fertilise/be carried to other plants

(c) Changing photoperiod can affect timing of/cause breeding/mating
or small mammals/example breed when photoperiod increasing
or large mammals/example breed when photoperiod decreasing

13. (a) Glycogen

(b) (i) X - insulin
      Y - glucagon
    (ii) Pancreas
    (iii) 1. Raised/High blood sugar/glucose level
       2. causes release of insulin/hormone X
       3. Insulin stimulates conversion of glucose to glycogen/storage carbohydrate.
       4. This moves blood sugar/glucose level back to normal/set point.

or
1. Reduced/Low blood sugar level causes
2. release of glucagons/hormone Y
3. Glucagon stimulates conversion of glycogen to glucose
4. blood sugar back to normal/set point.

or
1. Change detected
2. Corrective mechanism switched on
3. Return to set point/normal
4. Corrective mechanism is switched off

14. (*a*) (i) Succession
(ii) Grass alters/modifies the habitat/soil so that it is more suitable/favourable for shrubs

or
Grass increases humus/water retention/soil fertility/nutrient level/depth of soil
(iii) Diverse/high biomass/contains complex food webs

(*b*) (i) Density dependent - competition, predation, disease, food supply (A, B, D and F)
Density independent - rainfall, temperature (C, E)
(ii) Increases
Decreases

Section C

1A (i) *Any five points from the following:*
1. Occurs in cytoplasm
2. Glucose broken down to/converted to/ reduced to/oxidised to (two molecules of) pyruvic acid
3. C6 compound broken down to 2 X C3
4. Step by step breakdown by enzymes **or** series of enzyme controlled reactions
5. Net gain/production of ATP/explanation of net gain of ATP
6. NAD accepts hydrogen/NADH produced and transferred to cytochrome system/ cristae/electron transfer system
7. Oxygen not required/anaerobic. Occurs in aerobic and anaerobic conditions.

(ii) *Any five points from the following:*
8. Occurs in the mitochondrion matrix
9. Requires oxygen **or** aerobic phase
10. C2 acetyl group produced from pyruvic acid
11. Acetyl group joins with CoA
12. Acetyl CoA reacts/combines with a C4 compound to form C6 compound/citric acid
13. Cyclical series of reactions back to the C4 compound
14. Carbon dioxide produced/given off/ released
15. NAD accepts hydrogen/NADH produced and transferred to cytochrome system
16. Krebs cycle needs/requires/is controlled by enzymes

1B (i) *Any four points from the following:*
1. Carried out by phagocytes/monocytes/ macrophages
2. Non-specific
3. Bacteria/foreign material/virus engulfed/enveloped **or** description/ diagram
4. Into a vacuole/vesicle
5. Lysosomes fuse/join to vacuole **and** add enzymes to vacuole
6. Bacteria/foreign material/virus digested/ destroyed/broken down by enzymes

(ii) *Any four points from the following:*
7. Antibodies are proteins
8. They are produced by lymphocytes
9. Production stimulated by/in response to foreign/non-self antigens/proteins

10. Antibodies are specific/match the shape of antigens/lock and key diagram
11. Antibody renders harmless/destroys/ attacks/ combats/neutralises/combines with antigen

And two points from the following:
12. Transplanted tissues are antigenic/have foreign antigens/proteins recognised as foreign/non-self
13. Will be rejected/attacked by patient's antibodies **or** antibodies made against transplant tissue
14. Risk of rejection is reduced by suppressors/immunosuppressors/drugs which suppress/inhibit immune system **or** repressors which inhibit/suppress the immune system

2A *Any two points from the following:*
1. Fish (tissues)/body fluids hypertonic to surroundings **or** converse
2. Water enters fish through gills and/or mouth by osmosis
3. Potentially leading to bursting of/damage to cells **or** dilutes cytoplasm **or** increases water content of cells **or** excess water must be removed **or** water must be removed to keep water balance
4. Salts lost in urine/through mouth linings/gills

Any six points from the following:
5. Kidneys have many glomeruli
6. Kidneys have large glomeruli
7. Filtration rate of kidneys/glomeruli/blood is high
8. Urine produced is dilute
9. Large volume/amount/quantity of urine produced
10. Chloride secretory cells present in gills absorb salts
11. Against the concentration gradient/by active transport/uptake/actively

In question 2A, one mark is available for coherence and one mark is available for relevance.

Coherence
1. The writing must be under **sub-headings** or divided into **paragraphs** with a sub- heading/paragraph eg 'Problems and Adaptations'.
2. Answer should have at least **one** point from problems (1-4) and four points from adaptations (5 - 11)

Relevance
1. **Must not** give details of salt water fish/desert mammals
2. **Must** have given at least **one** point from problems and four points from adaptations.

2B *Any two points from the following:*
1. (Co-operative hunting means) animals/eg hunting in a social group/pack/team **or** means working together in hunting/to get food
2. Advantage eg larger prey/more successful, less energy used/pursuit time per individual, net gain of energy is greater than by foraging alone
3. Another different advantage from list

Any three points from the following:
4. Dominance hierarchy is a rank/pecking order within a social group
5. Consists of dominant/alpha and subordinate individuals
6. In feeding dominant/alpha individuals eat first (followed by subordinate) **or** dominant get bigger share of food **or** converse
7. Ensured survival of dominant when food scarce
8. Subordinate animal may gain more food than by foraging alone

And three points from the following:

9. Territory is (an area) marked/defended for feeding/hunting
10. Ensures a food supply/must contain enough food
    or the more food available the smaller the territory
    or converse
11. Territorial behaviour reduces competition
12. Energy expended in marking/patrolling/ defending
14. Gain of energy increased by lack of competition
    or foraging made more economical

In question 2B, one mark is available for coherence and one mark is available for relevance.

Coherence

1. The writing must be under **sub-headings** or divided into **paragraphs** with a sub- heading/paragraph eg 'Cooperative hunting/dominance hierarchy and territorial behaviour'.
2. Answer should have at least **five** points from cooperative hunting and dominace hierarchy (1-8) and two points from territorial behaviour (9 - 13)

Relevance

1. **Must not** give details of individual foraging, mating behaviour or social defence
2. **Must** have given at least **five** points from cooperative hunting and dominance hierarchy and two points from territorial behaviour.

HIGHER BIOLOGY 2008

Section A

1. C	2. A	3. A
4. A	5. D	6. C
7. B	8. D	9. A
10. D	11. B	12. D
13. B	14. C	15. B
16. B	17. D	18. C
19. C	20. C	21. D
22. A	23. A	24. C
25. B	26. D	27. D
28. B	29. A	30. C

Section B

1. (*a*) P granum/grana/thylakoid
    Q stroma

   (*b*) (i) Anywhere within a granum
       (ii) Widen/broaden the absorption/action spectrum
           or
           can absorb other parts of the spectrum
           or
           can photosynthesise using more/different colours (of light)/wavelengths (of light)
           or
           Absorbs light/wavelengths/colours not absorbed by chlorophyll

   (*c*) (i) ATP
           NADPH
           NADPH$_2$
           Hydrogen/H$_2$
       (ii) Glucose   6
           Carbon dioxide   1
           Glycerate phosphate (GP)   3
           Ribulose bisphosphate (RuBP)   5

   (*d*) (i) Light intensity
       (ii) Factor:
           Carbon dioxide/CO$_2$
           Justification:
           Greater increase in rate at increased % carbon dioxide (at same temp) than at increased temp (at same % carbon dioxide)
           or Use correct values from the graph

2. (*a*) (i) S protein
           T phospholipids
       (ii) Allows exit/export of mRNA (from nucleus) to cytoplasm/ribosomes/rough ER
           or
           Allows entry of mRNA to cytoplasm from nucleus
       (iii) (Presence of) large numbers of/many mitochondria

   (*b*) (i) Glucose/it moves from a high concentration to a low concentration (through the membrane)
           or
           Glucose/it moves down/with the concentration gradient
       (ii) Increases/maximum surface area
           For increased/maximum absorption/ diffusion/uptake/exchange (of glucose/ materials)
       (iii) Glycogen

3. (*a*) glucose
glycogen
amino acids
protein
carbohydrate

(*b*) (i) Cycle Y: Krebs/citric acid/TCA cycle
Compound Z: Carbon dioxide/CO_2
(ii) NAD

(*c*) Acts as final/terminal/last acceptor of hydrogen/H/H_2 (to form water)

(*d*) (i) Lactic acid
(ii) Cytoplasm
(iii) Transfers chemical energy
or
Transfers/transports/links energy from respiration/energy producing reactions to energy requiring reactions/processes/ examples

4. (*a*) True
False   phosphate
False   doubled

(*b*) Enzymes/polymerase
or DNA templates/parental strand of DNA
or ATP

(*c*) (i) 58%
(ii) 1080

5. (*a*) (i) As the (population) density/number of trees (per hectare) increases the (total volume of) resin decreases. But at high (population) densities/numbers of trees (per hectare) increasing density has little/no effect.
or converse
or use of correct values from table
or the lower the population the more resin produced
(ii) 3·5

(*b*) blocking holes/sealing wounds/isolating areas/localising areas/forming a protective barrier preventing entry of/spread of microorganisms/fungi/bacteria/pathogens/ infection/disease/viruses/parasites

6. (*a*) (i) • From 0/beginning - 40 days water loss decreases from 3·1cm^3 per hr per kg to 0·6/by 2·5
• 40 - 50 days increase from 0·6 to 0·9/by 0·3cm^3 per hr per kg
• 50 - 70 days decrease from 0·9 to 0·4/by 0·5cm^3 per hr per kg
(ii) 25%
(iii) 1 : 2
(iv) Reduces the (rate of) water loss/requirement for water/transpiration
or conserves/saves water
Cherry laurel/other broad leaved tree does not lose leaves and has higher (rate of) water loss

(*b*) (i) 3
(ii) 3·25-3·3
(iii) Wind (speed)/windiness/humidity/air pollution/air pressure/light intensity/air movement/hours of sunlight

7. (*a*) (i) Male grey
Female black
(ii) 1 Male GB, Gb, gB, gb
Female gB, gb
2 Correct offspring derived from gametes supplied
(iii) 4 : 3 : 1
or correct ratio from offspring given in 7(*a*)ii

(*b*) Male horse was homozygous/true breeding for white markings/homozygous dominant/TT

8. (*a*) (i) Cooperative (hunting)
Bigger prey can be obtained
or less energy used per individual
or subordinate/lower ranking animals may gain more food
or hunting more likely to be successful
or more food gained than by hunting alone
(ii) Dominance hierarchy
(iii) 1 More/adequate prey/food available
or reduces/less competition
or energy expended in defence of territory is less than energy gained from food

2 Population/number of wolves/size of wolf pack/number in pack
or level of competition from neighbouring packs
or food supply/prey density/population of prey

(*b*) (i) 81·5
(ii) Captive breeding
or cell/seed/gene/sperm banks

9. (*a*) 4

(*b*) Reach compensation point earlier in the day/at low light intensity
or can photosynthesise earlier in the day/at low light intensities/for longer each day
or net/overall gain of food produced earlier

10. (*a*) Although temperatures fall to $-10°C$/are reduced at night the camel's body temperature is maintained at about 36°C/higher than this.

(*b*) Endotherms

11. (*a*) 2500

(*b*) (i) Variety/type of barley
or Volume/mass of (water culture) solution
or Carbon dioxide concentration (of atmosphere)
or Concentration of other minerals/nutrients/ elements/named example
or pH
or oxygen concentration in solution
(ii) No soil to adhere to the roots and potentially affect mass determinations/ damage roots at harvest
or Control of nutrient (concentration) easier to achieve or difficult to achieve in soil
or disease less likely
(iii) Algae may use up/change the nutrient/ mineral/element levels of the solutions
or Prevents interspecific competition for ions/minerals/nutrients/elements
Fresh mass includes water which does not relate to growth
or dry mass is measure of actual biomass produced

(c) (i) and (ii)

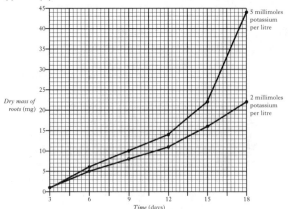

(d) Oxygen allows more (aerobic) respiration
(Aerobic) respiration produces more ATP/energy
For more active uptake/transport of K

12. (a) (i) Produces (new) cells/tissue/xylem/phloem
or is the site of mitosis/cell division
or is a meristem
(ii) Xylem

(b) (Caterpillars) eat/reduce/remove leaves/leaf surfaces
Less photosynthesis
Less energy/food/materials available for growth/to produce xylem

13. (a) (i) Drinking water/intake of water/watery fluid
(ii) Hypothalamus
(iii) Name: X antidiuretic hormone/ADH
Effect: Increases kidney tubule permeability to water

(b) Change from set point/normal/certain limits is detected/picked up by receptors
Corrective mechanism switched on/effectors respond
(Correction results in) return to set point/normal Corrective mechanism switched off
or Use of a specific example including all the above points

14. (a) 13 or less hours of light per day
or Photoperiod of 13 hours or less
or Maximum of 13 hours of light per day
or 11 or more hours of dark per day

(b) Young born February/March/April/Spring
and
Description of favourable conditions eg
sufficient food/suitable temperatures/lower rainfall
or offspring have time for growth before winter
or offspring not born in winter when temps too low

(c) Photoperiodism/photoperiodic behaviour

Section C

1. **A.** (i) *Any six points from the following:*
1. the regulator gene produces/codes for repressor (molecule/substance/ protein)
2. lactose is the inducer
3. lactose binds with repressor (molecule/substance/protein)
4. in the presence of lactose operator switches on structural gene
5. in the presence of lactose/so enzyme/ B galactosidase made
or structural gene codes for enzyme
6. in absence of lactose repressor (molecule/substance/protein) binds to operator

7. in the absence of lactose operator cannot switch on/switches off structural gene
8. in the absence of lactose/so/when structural gene switched off and enzyme not made
9. (*E. coli*) conserves resources/energy
or does not waste energy

(ii) *Any four points from the following:*
10. phenylalanine is involved in a metabolic pathway
or show in diagram of pathway
11. each step (in a metabolic pathway) is controlled by an enzyme
12. PKU is caused by mutation (of a gene)/ inborn error of metabolism and leads to an altered/absent enzyme
13. phenylalanine builds up/is not broken down/ is converted to a toxic compound/ phenylpyruvate
14. damage to nervous system development/ description, eg brain damage/mental retardation/learning difficulties

B. (i) *Any five points from the following:*
1. if population density increases factor has more/increased/intensified effect **or** converse
2. Factors include (*any two from*):
   • disease/infection/parasites
   • food supply/availability/shortage
   • predation
   • toxic waste made by organism
   • competition for food/space/habitat
3. a third factor
4. when population (density) increases then named factor increases
or when population (density) increases then food supply decreases
or converses
5. their effect is to decrease population (density)
6. effect tends to return population to a stable size/carrying capacity/size environment can sustain

(ii) *Any five points from the following:*
7. succession is the sequence of plant communities inhabiting an area
or description
8. succession is unidirectional
or arrow in diagram labelled succession/time/years
9. communities/populations/plants modify the habitat/increase soil fertility/making it more suitable for subsequent/other/new communities/populations/plants
10. later communities/climax community has greater/est species diversity
11. later communities/climax community have more complex food webs
12. later communities/climax community have greater/est biomass
13. the final community is the climax community

2. **A.** *Any six points from the following:*
1. gene mutations alter the base/nucleotide type/sequence/order of DNA
2. they include (*any two from*): inversion, substitution, insertion and deletion
3. remaining two
4. Any two descriptions from description of a gene mutation including reference to bases/ nucleotides
or diagrams with bases labelled
5. remaining two descriptions
6. inversion/substitution affect only one/two triplets/few bases/are point mutations

7. and so only slightly alter/alter few amino acids in the amino acid sequence of the protein

8. insertion/deletion affect many/all triplets after the mutation/are frame-shift mutations

9. and so affect many amino acids in a protein/all amino acids after the mutation

And two points from the following:

10. mutagenic agents cause/induce/increase the rate/frequency/chance/likelihood of mutation

11. they include (ir)radiation/examples/chemical (agent)s/examples

Coherence

- divided into clear sections
- At least 4 points on gene mutation
- And at least 1 point on mutagenic agents

Relevance

- no mention of chromosome mutations, polyploidy, non-disjunction
- At least 4 points on gene mutation
- And at least 1 point on mutagenic agents

2. **B.** *Any five points from the following:*

1. somatic fusion overcomes sexual incompatibility (in plants)

2. plant cells have their cell walls removed/broken down/destroyed/digested (membrane agents)

3. using cellulase

4. resulting in protoplasts

5. which then fuse/join

6. fused protoplast (cultured to) produce new plant/a callus

And four points from the following:

7. genes located/found on chromosomes by gene probes/banding patterns

8. endonucleases/restriction enzymes used to cut DNA/genes (from donor chromosomes)

9. plasmids extracted/isolated/removed **and** opened/cut open using restriction enzymes/endonuclease

10. genes sealed/inserted into bacterial genome/plasmid using ligase

11. altered plasmid placed into bacterial cell

12. engineered/altered bacteria cultured/multiply and produce new protein/product/insulin/HGH

Coherence

- Divided into clear sections
- At least 2 points on somatic fusion
- And at least 2 points on genetic engineering
- Total of 5 points required

Relevance

- No mention of GM crops, selective breeding, details of diabetes or dwarfism etc
- At least 2 points on somatic fusion
- And at least 2 points on genetic engineering
- Total of 5 points required

HIGHER BIOLOGY 2009

Section A

1.	B	16.	B
2.	A	17.	C
3.	D	18.	D
4.	B	19.	A
5.	B	20.	D
6.	C	21.	D
7.	C	22.	B
8.	D	23.	D
9.	B	24.	A
10.	B	25.	C
11.	C	26.	A
12.	A	27.	A
13.	D	28.	C
14.	A	29.	C
15.	C	30.	D

Section B

1. (*a*) Y transmitted/transmission/transmit

   Z reflected/reflection/reflect (both)

   (*b*) (i) Chlorophyll/chlorophyll a/chlorophyll b

   (ii) Widen/broaden absorption spectrum
   OR

Absorb	different	colours/named colours
Use	other	wavelengths

   AND pass energy on to chlorophyll

   (*c*) (i) Stroma (of chloroplast)

   (ii) To reduce/reduction of GP/CO_2

   (*d*) P temperature
   Q carbon dioxide/CO_2 (concentration)
   R temperature
   OR light intensity

2. (*a*) (i) W oxygen/O_2
   X acetyl (group)
   Y carbon dioxide/CO_2

   (ii) 6

   (*b*) (i) 10 hours

   (ii) 3·5

3. (*a*) (i) Translation

   (ii) Peptide

   (iii) 1 proline
   4 glycine

   (*b*) (Many) Golgi apparatus/vesicles/bodies

4. (*a*) (i) Protein (coat)

   (ii) Virus takes over cell/host metabolism

   (iii) *Any two from:*
   1. viral nucleic acid/DNA/RNA transcribed to/directs synthesis of mRNA
   2. mRNA translated into protein coats
   3. viruses assembled/put together

(b) (i) (Foreign) Antigen

    (ii) 1. 3·75 times

        2. 1. (Response) is quicker/faster/took less time

           2. (Antibody concentration) remains high for longer/decreased slower/maintained at higher level for longer

5. (a) (i) 88%

    (ii) 88:19:4

(b) Pair A

Different numbers/less of woodrats **AND** brush mice in diet

(c) (i) Increases/changes from 3·6 to 4·0 in summer (of year 1) then decreases/changes from 4·0 to 2·0 in winter (of year 2)

Then increases/changes from 2·0 to 3·2 (in spring of year 2)

    (ii) 52%

(d) 20g

(e) In winter number **AND** biomass of prey is less so have bigger territory

6. (a) Ovaries/testes

(b) (i) Chiasma/ata

    (ii) R and T

        T and R

    (iii) Independent assortment/segregation/alignment **OR** Random segregation/assortment/alignment

(c) 40

7. (a) (i) BE, Be, bE, be

    (ii) 1 black: 1 chocolate: 2 yellow

(b) bbEE/EEbb

8. (a) (i) As the cuticle thickness increases up to 5·6 (micrometers) the rate of water loss decreases = 1

But further increase in cuticle thickness causes very little/no difference in rate of water loss = 1

    (ii) Turgid

    (iii) Increased temperature/warmer **OR** increased wind speed/windiness/windy conditions **OR** windier

(b) (i) Reduces air movements **OR** traps water vapour/moist air/increased humidity = 1

fewer stomata **OR** smaller surface area for evaporation/transpiration = 1

    (ii) Xerophytes/xerophytic

9. (a) (i) Biomass reduced because grass has been eaten/grazed/removed

Increased diversity because reduced competition allows less vigorous/less dominant to survive/colonise/move in **AND**

allows others/less vigorous/less dominant to survive/colonise/move in

    (ii) Reduce/decrease the diversity

Some species would be completely eaten/unable to recover from grazing

(b) Ticks at dandelions and couch grass only

Plant adaptation	Tick (✓)
Dandelions have deep roots	✓
Wild roses have thorns	
Couch grass has underground stems	✓
Nettles have stings	
Tobacco plants produce nicotine	

10. (a) (i) *Any two from:*
- Volume of extract/solution/sample
- pH (of solutions)
- time left in colorimeter/out of water bath

    (ii) Shows what would happen without the lead ethanoate **OR** that lead ethanoate is causing the effect/inhibiting the enzyme

(b) Some reaction occurred immediately **OR** Enzyme started working before lead added **OR** Browning occurred before reading taken **OR** Pigment produced as soon as cut up

(c) (i) Appropriate enclosed scales with zeros and labels from table

    (ii) Correct plots joined by straight lines and correct label from table

(d) As concentration increases, the activity (of the enzyme) decreases/effect of enzyme decreases/the enzyme is inhibited more

(e) Any figure from 1·6 and less than 2·0
Enzyme has been denatured

11. (a) They share/have a common ancestor/the same ancestor/have evolved from a single species **AND** different mouths/heads (shapes) for different food/feeding methods

(b) They would be unable to interbreed/breed together to produce fertile offspring **OR** if they interbreed they produce sterile offspring

(c) (i) Ecological **OR** reproductive

    (ii) Prevents gene/exchange/flow **OR** prevents breeding between populations/sub-populations

12. (a) L

(b) Xylem

(c) Spring
xylem (cells) produced last were wider

13. (a) Regulator (gene)

(b) Lactose

(c) (i) 1. Repressor (molecule) binds to/attaches/binds/joins with/blocks operator

        2. Operator switches off structural gene

        3. Enzyme/(β) galactosidase not made

    (ii) Saves energy/ATP/resources

14. (a) (i) Iron needed for haemoglobin **AND** haemoglobin carries oxygen (to tissues)

    (ii) Reduced/retarded/stunted growth **OR** low birthweight **AND** reduced mental development

(b) (i) Decreasing photoperiod/description of decreasing photoperiod

(ii) Offspring born in spring/summer when weather/food supply more favourable

15. (a) Succession

(b) Makes soil more fertile/deeper/thicker

OR soil has more nutrients/minerals/ions/humus/organic matter

OR soil has better drainage/more aeration/better water retention

(c) Greater than

Community Y (both needed)

Section C

1A *Any four points from the following:*

(i) 1. contains protein
2. contains phospholipid
3. bilayer/double layer/two layers of phospholipids
4. phospholipids are fluid/constantly moving
5. protein arranged as a mosaic/patchy pattern/scattered/interspersed
5a. fluid mosaic pattern/model **(only award if 4 or 5 not scored)**
6. has channel forming proteins/pores

Any three points from the following:

(ii) 7. carriers/bind ions/molecules/proteins **AND** move/carry/them across membrane
8. ion/molecule uptake is selective **OR** description
9. low to high concentration **OR** against concentration gradient
10. requires energy/ATP

Any three points from the following

(iii) 11. made of cellulose fibres
12. fully/freely permeable
13. provides support/rigidity for cells/plants **OR** gives cell shape
14. stops cells bursting after water uptake/when turgid/when placed in hypotonic solution

1B (i) *Any six points from the following:*

1. double helix
2. two chains/strands of nucleotides
3. deoxyribose sugar, phosphate and base make up a nucleotide
4. nucleotides joined together by sugar - phosphates bonds **OR** sugar and phosphate joined to form backbones/chains/strands
5. base names (all four)
6. complementary bases pair
7. (weak) hydrogen bonding between bases

Any three points from the following:

(ii) 8. the molecule unwinds/uncoils/untwists **AND** unzips/H bonds between bases break
9. base pairing of (free) DNA nucleotides with complementary partners
10. sugar-phosphate bonds/backbones form
11. rewinds into two double helices **OR** two double helices form
12. requires enzymes **OR** ATP

Any one point from:

13. identical OR exactly the same DNA/molecules/copies produced
14. ensures daughter/new cells have complete/correct/the same genetic information

2A *Any four points from the following:*

1. nitrogen for amino acid/protein/enzymes
2. nitrogen for bases of nucleic acids/DNA/RNA/nucleotides
3. nitrogen for chlorophyll

OR plant deficient in nitrogen will not have any chlorophyll

4. phosphorus for nucleic acids/DNA/RNA/RuBP/NADP/GP/ATP
5. magnesium for chlorophyll **OR** plant deficient in magnesium will not have any chlorophyll

Any four points from:

6. nitrogen deficiency produces chlorosis/yellow leaves/pale green leaves
7. nitrogen deficiency produces red leaf bases
8. nitrogen deficiency produces long roots
9. phosphorus deficiency produces red leaf bases
10. magnesium deficiency produces chlorosis
11. nitrogen/phosphorus/magnesium deficiency stunts/reduces/retards/restricts growth

Coherence
- divided into clear sections (including tabulation)
- must be 5 points in total
- At least 2/3 points on use of elements and at least 2/3 points on deficiency symptoms
- Total of three points required

Relevance
- no mention of other elements eg potassium or effects of light eg etiolation
- must be 5 points in total
- At least 2/3 points on use of elements and at least 2/3 points on deficiency symptoms
- Total of three points required

2B *Any two points from the following:*

1. they include disease/parasites, food supply/lack of food/competition for food, predation, competition for space/territory/shelter, toxic waste produced by organisms (any 2)
2. a third factor

And four points from:

3. increasing population/number of animals intensifies/increases the effect of density-dependent factors (or converse)
4. at higher pops   – more/easier spread of disease/parasites
5. – less food available/more competition for food
6. – more predation/predators
7. – more competition for space/territory/shelter
8. – more toxic wastes from organism
9. this reduces population
10. reduced effect of factor allows population to rise again
11. result is that populations/numbers remain stable/are regulated

And two points from:

12. include temperature/rainfall/natural events eg flood/fire/earthquake/drought/rain storm/desertification/deforestation (any 2)
13. increasing population size does not intensify/increase the effect of density-independent factors
14. can cause extreme changes to population sizes

Coherence
- divided into clear sections
- At least 4 points on density dependent
- And at least 1 point on density independent
- Total of five points required

Relevance
• no mention of eg monitoring populations or conservation
• At least 4 points on density dependent
• And at least 1 point on density independent
• Total of five points required

HIGHER BIOLOGY 2010

Section A

1.	D	16.	C
2.	B	17.	D
3.	C	18.	D
4.	B	19.	A
5.	C	20.	B
6.	D	21.	C
7.	A	22.	C
8.	D	23.	A
9.	D	24.	D
10.	D	25.	A
11.	A	26.	B
12.	B	27.	C
13.	C	28.	A
14.	B	29.	C
15.	B	30.	A

Section B

1. (a) Protein, phospholipids, porous, selectively

   (b) (i) 46.5 units (+/- 0.5)
       (ii) 800 µg per hour
       (iii)
           1. Respiration provides the energy/for uptake/
                                    ATP   active
                                               transport

           2. Cyanide   reduces   respiration (enzymes)
                        inhibits/ energy/ATP release
                        stops/
                        prevents

           3. (More) cyanide gives decreased   uptake/
                              prevents/stops   active
                                                   transport

              or

              Less energy/ATP gives decreased   uptake/
                               prevents/stops   active
                                                   transport

2. (a) (On surface of/in/on) grana/granum

   (b) Species – B
       Explanation:
       More   accessory pigment/
       Higher mass of   carotene and xanthophyll
       allows absorption of light transmitted/ reflected (by other
                                   plants)
                                   not absorbed (by other plants)

   (c) (i) A – carbon dioxide/CO_2
           B – glucose/carbohydrate
       (ii) Reduces/reduction of GP/CO_2
       (iii) RuBP 5
             GP 3
       (iv) RuBP decrease
            GP   increase/more/accumulates
            Explanation: No/less ATP/NADPH available

3. (a) (i) 7.5 grams per litre
       (ii) 0.2 grams per litre per minute

(b) (i) 1. Anaerobic respiration   produces ethanol
       Anaerobic conditions
       Fermentation
   2. Oxygen (in air)   starts aerobic respiration/
                        stops anaerobic respiration/
                        stops fermentation

(ii) The ethanol   has poisoned/   the yeast
     Concentration   killed/become
                     lethal to

or

all glucose/food/respiratory substrate used up

4. (a) (i) X − deoxyribose
           Y − phosphate
       (ii) 1. cytosine/C
            2. thymine/T
       (iii) Enzyme(s) **or** (DNA) polymerase = **1**
             ATP = **1**
       (iv) Cell division **or** mitosis **or** meiosis

(b) TAG

5. (a) (i) Lymphocytes
       (ii) (foreign) antigen

(b) (i) 1 : 3 : 4
    (ii) Black
    (iii) The more tannin /the greater the tannin content the
          less fungus/leaf area covered
          or use values from the table
    (iv) (Fresh mass includes) water which can
         change/vary/fluctuate

6. (a) (i) (As distance increases) from 500 to 2500m the number
           of dances decreases from 6 to 3/falls by 3 = **1**
           (when distance increased) from 2500 to 5000m the
           number decreased from 3 to 2/falls by 1 = **1**
           or (500 m to 5000m dances drop from 6 to 2) = **1**
       (ii) 1.25s
       (iii) 500%
       (iv) 6s

(b) (i) 2.5
    (ii) 3500m

(c) (i) Direction **or** quantity **or** quality (of food)
    (ii) Reduces/saves the energy spent in foraging/ finding
         food
         or ensures a net energy gain **or** description of net
         energy gain
         or conserves energy by going straight to food source

7. (a) Same genes/sequence of genes/order of genes
       or genes match gene for gene

(b) (i) Chiasma(ta)
    (ii) Increases   variation
         or
         Allows   new combinations of alleles

(c) (i) Abcd P only
        aBCD P only
        AbcD P and Q
        aBCd P and Q
    (ii) abcD **or** ABCd **or** reverses

8. (a) (i) Affected female X^RX^R and X^RX^r
           Unaffected female X^rX^r = **1**
       (ii) 50%
       (iii) Substitution
             One amino acid altered

(b)   Promotes the absorption/uptake of <u>calcium</u> from the
       intestine

9. (a) Problem
       lose water by osmosis
       or cells/tissue/fish hypotonic to sea/surroundings
       or sea/surroundings hypertonic to cells/tissue/fish
       or higher water concentration in fish than sea/surroundings
       Fish Physiological
       chloride secretory cells secrete/get rid of salt/ions
       or (kidney with) few/small glomeruli
       or low kidney filtration rate
       or slow kidney filtration
       Rat Behavioural
       Nocturnal/active/feeds at night
       or remain in burrow by day
       Rat Physiological
       • no sweat glands/sweating
       • colon/large intestine efficient at absorbing water
       • long loops of Henle **or** kidney tubules allow high
         reabsorption of water
       • high level of ADH

(b) Allow leaf/plant to float **or** make it buoyant **or** prevent it
    sinking **or** keeps it at the surface
    and To keep it in light for photosynthesis
    or To allow gas exchange through the stomata

10. (a) (i) Diameter/size/mass/number/surface area of beads **or**
            type of gel **or** time tap kept open **or**
            strain/concentration/mass/batch of *E.coli*
            or same volume of solution collected
        (ii) Same/identical funnel with gel beads without *E. Coli*
             To show *E.coli* produced the enzyme/
                      lactose did not beak down alone/
                      E.coli is the factor affecting lactose/
                      lactose is broken down by β galactosidase

(b) Scales and labels = **1**
    Plots and line = **1**

(c) 0.04 grams per minute

(d) *Any two from:*
    Repressor joins with lactose/inducer
    or Operator switches on structural gene
    or Structural gene produces enzyme/ β galactosidase
    or Time needed to breakdown lactose
    or
    Enzyme being induced/produced/made/released = **1**
    Time needed to breakdown lactose = **1**

(e) Saves/does not waste energy/ATP
    or saves/does not waste resources

11. (a) (i) 3-4 weeks and 4-5 weeks
        (ii) A
        (iii) Photosynthesis
        (iv) Dispersal of seeds/fruits **or** decomposition

(b) length/thickness/width of stem/shoots/roots/ internodes
    or height/length of plant
    or number of leaves

(c) (Apical) meristem

12. (a) Gene mutation
(b) Gain tyrosine from diet/food
    and   can be converted to pigment/
               enzyme 3 still working/present
(c) controls metabolic rate/metabolism

13. (a) B − Nitrogen   protein (synthesis)/enzymes/ amino
                           acids/nucleic acids/
                           RNA/DNA/ATP/chlorophyll/
                           NAD/NADP

           C − Magnesium

(b) **Term** – Etiolated/etiolation
Long stems/internodes
or yellow/pale/small/curled/chlorotic leaves

14. (a) (i) 22.5 **or** 23 beetles per m^2
(ii) Food (supply) **or** predators **or** disease
or competition for food/space
Rainfall/drought/flooding **or** temperature **or**
pesticide/insecticide **or** named natural disaster eg
(forest) fire

(b) *Any two from:*
(Conservation/management of) endangered species
(Conservation/management of) food species/source
(Conservation/management of) raw material species/source
Indicate levels of pollution

Section C

1A *Any six points from the following:*
(i) 1. IAA Stimulates/promotes cell division/mitosis
2. IAA Stimulates/promotes cell elongation
3. IAA Stimulates/promotes differentiation
4. IAA causes apical dominance/inhibits (growth of) lateral buds
5. IAA is important/involved in tropic effects/ tropisms/geotropism/phototropism
6. IAA causes shoot/plant growth towards light **or** description
7. Low/fall in/decrease in IAA (concentration) causes abscission/leaf fall **or** converse
8. IAA causes fruit formation/development/ growth

Any four points from the following:
(ii) 9. GA produced in embryo
10. GA travels to aleurone layer
11. GA stimulates/induces/switches on gene for production of (α-)amylase in aleurone layer
12. (α-)amylase breaks down/digests starch to maltose
13. maltose required for respiration/ATP production
14. GA breaks dormancy (of seeds)

1B *Any two points from the following:*
(i) 1. endotherms can regulate/control/maintain their (body) temperature (physiologically)
and ectotherms cannot/ectotherms temperature is dependent on their environment/behaviour
2. endotherms derive (most body) heat from respiration/metabolism/chemical reactions
3 ectotherms derive/get (body) heat from surroundings/environment **or** description of behaviour

Any eight points from the following:
(ii) 4. temperature monitoring centre/ thermoreceptors in hypothalamus
5. nerve message sent to skin/effectors
6. vasodilation/widening of blood vessels to skin in response to increased temperature
or vasoconstriction/narrowing of blood vessels to skin in response to decreased temperature
7. more/less blood to skin/extremities **or** less/more blood in body core
8. increased/more **or** decreased/less heat radiated from skin/extremities
9. increased temperature leads to (increase in) sweat production **or** converse
10. increase in heat loss due to evaporation of (water in) sweat **or** converse
11. Decrease in temperature causes hair erector muscles to raise/erect hair

12. traps (warm) air **or** forms insulating layer
13. Decrease in temperature causes muscle contraction/shivering which generates heat/raises body temperature
14. temperature regulation involves/is an example of negative feedback

2A *Any two points from the following:*
1. isolating mechanisms prevent gene flow between (sub-) populations/groups **or**
isolating mechanisms are barriers to gene exchange between/breeding between\mutations being passed between
or isolating mechanisms split a gene pool
2. geographic, ecological, reproductive (any two)
3. third

Any two points from:
4. mutations occur randomly
5. different mutations occur in each (sub-) population/group
6. Mutations increase/decrease survival
or mutations can be beneficial
or mutations can provide a selective advantage

Any two points from:
7. different conditions/habitat/environment exist for each (sub-)population
8. natural selection acts differently on/there are different selection pressures on each (sub-)population/groups
9. surviving/best suited/fittest individuals are able to breed/pass on (favourable) genes/alleles/mutations
10. over long periods after many generations
11. new species formed/speciation has occurred
12. new species are unable to interbreed/breed together to produce fertile young

Coherence
• divided into 3 clear sections
• At least 1/2 points on isolation (Points 1 – 3)
• At least 1/2 points on mutation (Points 4 – 6)
• And at least 2/3 points on natural selection (Points 7 – 12)
• total of five points required

Relevance
• no mention of artificial selection
• At least 1/2 points on isolation (Points 1 – 3)
• And at least 1/2 points on mutation (Points 4 – 6)
• And at least 2/3 points on natural selection (Points 7 – 12)
• total of five points required

2B *Any six points from the following:*
1. water moves into root (hair cells)by osmosis/from HWC to LWC/down water concentration gradient
2. water moves across/enters the cortex by osmosis/from HWC to LWC/down water concentration gradient
3. water enters xylem
4. water moves through xylem(vessels)
5. cohesion is attraction between/sticking together of water molecules
6. adhesion is attraction between water (molecules) and xylem (walls)/sticking of water molecules to xylem
5a. adhesion and cohesion named (if neither 5 nor 6 is scored)
7. water moves into leaf cells by osmosis/from HWC to LWC /down a water concentration gradient
8. water evaporates into (leaf) air spaces
9. water vapour diffuses from leaf surfaces/ lost through stomata

Any two points from:
10. water (provides raw material) for photosynthesis/photolysis
11. water provides turgidity/keeps cells turgid
12. causes cooling/cools the plant
13. minerals/nutrients/ions supplied/transported

Coherence
- Divided into clear sections
- At least 4 points on transpiration stream (Points 1 – 9)
- And at least 1 point on importance (Points 10 – 13)
- total of five points required

Relevance
- No mention of details of xerophytes or hydrophytes, mineral deficiencies
- At least 4 points on transpiration stream (Points 1 – 9)
- And at least 1 point on importance (Points 10 – 13)
- total of five points required

HIGHER BIOLOGY 2011

Section A

1.	C	16.	C
2.	A	17.	B
3.	C	18.	A
4.	D	19.	B
5.	B	20.	C
6.	D	21.	C
7.	C	22.	D
8.	A	23.	A
9.	A	24.	B
10.	D	25.	B
11.	B	26.	C
12.	B	27.	D
13.	D	28.	C
14.	D	29.	A
15.	A	30.	D

Section B

1. (*a*) P mitochondrion/mitochondria

Q (cavity of) Golgi (apparatus/body)
or smooth ER

(*b*) (i) 1. Protein
2. Phospholipid (either way round)

(ii) Selectively/semi permeable
or description based on comparison of molecular size

(*c*) Hypotonic

(*d*) 1. Draws food/particles/micro-organisms in using cilia
or moves to food/particles/microorganism using cilia

2. Encloses food into a (food) vacuole/vesicle
Engulfs particles
Seals in micro-organisms
or endocytosis

3. Lysosomes fuse with/attach to (food) vacuole
4. Digests food with enzymes from lysosomes
Breaks down particles

2. (*a*) Cytoplasm

(*b*) Enzymes **or** ATP **or** ADP **or** NAD **or** Pi

(*c*) R pyruvic acid/pyruvate
S ethanol/alcohol

(*d*) <u>Oxygen</u> needed as a final/last/terminal acceptor of hydrogen

3. (*a*) 1440

(*b*) Oxygen is no longer limiting/a limiting factor
or
Another factor/temp/glucose/respiratory substrate is limiting
or
ATP production/aerobic respiration has reached the maximum
or potassium uptake is at its maximum

(c) 1. Enzyme activity less/now reduced
or 20°C/temp/conditions not optimum for enzymes/ below optimum for enzymes
2. ATP production/respiration requires enzymes
or mention of respiratory enzymes
3. Less energy/ATP available/released/produced
4. Active uptake/transport requires energy
or potassium upake is active/requires energy

4. (a) (i) Photosynthesis occurs in wavelengths/colours of light/ green/yellow light/regions of spectrum little absorbed by the pigment/pigment shown/ chlorophyll
or Photosynthesis occurs when absorption of green/yellow/by the pigment is low
or Photosynthesis occurs in all colours but the pigment absorbs mainly blue and red/little yellow/ green (light)

(ii) (Paper/thin layer) chromatography

(b) 1. Photosynthesis occurs in red and blue light
2. Photosynthesis produces oxygen
3. (Aerobic) bacteria go to areas where oxygen is most abundant

5. (a) (i)

	X^R	X^r
X^r	$X^R X^r$	$X^r X^r$
Y	$X^R Y$	$X^r Y$

(ii) All boxes ticked

(iii) Fertilisation/Fusion of gametes is a random/chance process
or sample size/offspring number too small

(b) NKML **or** LMKN

6. (a) (i) 1. From 0 to 5 days/for the first 5 days it remains constant/stays at 1375 units
2. From 5 to 15 days/next 10 days drops to 450 units/falls by 925 units
3. **or** From 15 to 25 days/for next 10 days/for remaining days stays constant at 450 units

(ii) 60

(iii) 50

(iv) It would never reach its compensation point
or Compensation point greater than 400 (units)
or Lowest compensation point is 500 (units)
or Compensation point levels off at 500 (units)
or Needs more than/at least 500 (units) to grow

No net energy gain
or respiration would exceed photosynthesis
or more carbohydrate/glucose/food used than gained

(b) (i) Spider plant
Reason Spider plant has compensation points of 250 units at day 20 and/or 500 units at day 10 in Graph 1/ the other Graph
or
The compensation points (in Graph 2) match compensation point in Graph 1

(ii) 1.75 times

7. (a) (i) AUG

(ii) Second base is G/guanine
or guanine in second/centre position
or contains guanine
or None have uracil/U

(b) Isoleucine, glutamine

8. (a) Radiation/example of radiation

(b) (i) Insertion
Deletion
Substitution
Inversion

(ii) Gene mutation numbers 1 and 2

Explanation:
Will affect many codons/triplets/amino acids
or
They will affect every codon/triplet/amino acid after the mutation/from that point on

9. (a) (i) Bring down/kill larger prey
or Increases hunting success/better chance of catching prey
or Less energy expended per individual
or Greater net gain of energy per individual

Reduces/less (inter/intra) competition

(ii) Ensures that energy gained in food is greater than energy expended in catching food/hunting food/ foraging
or converse

(iii) Numbers confuse the predator/lion
or Individuals take turns at watching for predators/lions
or More chance that at least one individual will see predator/lion
or More chance of spotting/getting warning about predator/lion
or Description of group protection in wildebeest
or Harder to single out individual

(b) (i) Avoidance (behaviour)

(ii) Reduces chances of being eaten
or reduces predation
or Protection from predators

10. (a) Temperature **or** variety/type/species/age of rice (grains)

(b) (i) Shows that it is GA which is causing the results/germination/breaking of dormancy
or shows results without GA to compare to others/those with GA

(ii) Some GA is already present in (rice) grains/seeds/ embryo
or (rice) grains/seeds/embryo produces GA

(c) Use of 50 (rice) grains at each concentration/each time/in each solution/in each beaker

(d) Increased
Reason   evaporation of water/solvent

(e) 42

(f) Scales – both need 0s, at least half grid used

Labels – from table
Plot – accurate plots and straight lines

(g) 1. Increasing GA concentration increases germination/number germinating
or increasing GA concentration above 30 mg per litre has little effect on rate of germination
or between 5 and 10 mg per litre of GA greatest increase in germination/number germinated

2. The longer in GA (solution) the greater germination/number germinating

(h) Aleurone (layer)

11. (a) A and B

moult	allows	increases in length
exoskeleton/skin shed	is followed by	inflation
		growth

B and C
exoskeleton/skin prevents increase in length
or restricts/limits/inhibits growth

(b) (i) X Growth hormone/GH/somatotrophin
Y Thyroid stimulating hormone/TSH

(ii) Thyroid

(iii) Controls/increases/regulates/stimulates the metabolic rate/metabolism/metabolic processes

12. (a) (i) As galactosidase/enzyme increases/is produced/appears/is introduced the lactose decreases
or lactose begins to fall/decrease after galactosidase levels increase/starts to be produced

(ii) True
False
True

(b) Undifferentiated
Genes
Limited

13. (a) H
B F
B D
A

(b) E, A

14. (a) Hypothalamus – B/water and C/temperature
Pancreas – A/glucose

(b) 1. Glucagon
2. Adrenaline/epinephrine

(c) Decrease the permeability (of kidney tubule cells) to water

(d) (i) Vasoconstriction/constriction/narrowing of diameter

Less/inhibits/reduces blood flow to skin so less heat is lost by <u>radiation</u>

(ii) Endotherms

Section C

1A *Any six points from the following:*
(i) 1. fish (tissues) hypotonic to/at higher water concentration than sea water/surroundings/ environment **or** converse
2. water loss by osmosis through mouth/gills
3. drinks sea/salt water
4. chloride secretory cells in gills secrete/excrete/remove/ get rid of salt
5. by active transport/actively/against concentration gradient
6. (kidneys have) few small glomeruli
7. slow filtration/low rate of filtration
8. low volume/amount of concentrated urine

Any four points from the following:
(ii) 9. behavioural and physiological (mechanisms)
10. active by night/nocturnal **or** stays in (damp/humid) burrow by day
11. dry faeces **or** efficient absorption of water by large intestine
12 does not sweat/no sweat glands **or** dry mouth and nasal passages
13. long loops of Henle/kidney tubules so high/more/ increased reabsorption of water
or high/increased levels of ADH so high/more/ increased reabsorption water
14. low volumes/amounts of concentrated urine

1B *Any four points from the following:*
(i) 1. gamete mother cells (undergo meiosis)
2. spindle forms **or** nuclear membrane breaks down
3. homologous chromosomes pair
4. homologous chromosomes line up at equator/middle of cell
or crossing over occurs at chiasmata
5. homologous chromosomes segregate/move apart
or independent assortment occurs
6. Cytoplasm splits/new nuclear membranes form
7. two haploid cells/cells with one set of chromosomes/ cells with half the number of chromosomes form

Any three points from the following:
8. two new spindles form
9. chromosomes line up on equator/middle of cell
10. chromatids separate/are pulled apart
11. cytoplasm splits/new nuclear membranes form
12. to give four haploid cells/gametes

Any three points from the following:
(ii) 13. Independent/random assortment **or** description of independent assortment
14. crossing over
15. recombination **or** description of recombination
16. non-disjunction/description

2A *Any six from the following:*

1. occurs in stroma of chloroplasts
2. carbon dioxide/CO_2 accepted by RuBP to produce GP/PGA
3. glucose C6, RuBP 5C and GP/PGA 3C
4. NADP carries/supplies hydrogen to Calvin cycle/carbon fixation stage
5. H/H2/Hydrogen reduces GP/PGA/carbon dioxide/CO2 to glucose/carbohydrate
6. ATP provides energy
7. GP/PGA used to regenerate/make/generate/produce RuBP
8. enzyme controlled/requires enzymes

Any two from the following:

9. energy in carbohydrate/glucose
   or produces glucose for respiration
10. produces cellulose **or** structural carbohydrate **or** carbohydrate for cell walls
11. produces storage carbohydrate **or** starch
12. major biological molecules **or** protein, fat, lipid, nucleic acid, nucleotides are derived/produced/ made

Coherence

- Divided into clear sections
- At least 3/4 points on carbon fixation
- And at least 1/2 points on significance
- *Total of five points required*

Reference

- No mention of details of light dependent stage other than ATP/NADPH supplied by this stage
- At least 3/4 points on carbon fixation
- And at least 1/2 points on significance
- *Total of five points required*

2B *Any five points from the following:*

1. virus attaches stick/joins/adheres to (host) cell
2. viral nucleic acid/DNA/RNA/virus enters/injected in
3. viral nucleic acid/DNA/RNA/virus takes over/alters cell metabolism
   or viral nucleic acid/DNA/RNA/virus alters cell instructions
4. viral nucleic acid/DNA/RNA replicated
5. protein coats synthesised/produced
6. (host) cell supplies nucleotides/enzymes/ATP/amino acids
7. (new) viruses assembled/or description
8. (new) viruses released by (host) cell bursting/lysis

Any three from the following:

9. lymphocytes produce antibodies
10. antibodies produced in response to foreign/non-self antigens
11. antibodies are specific to antigens
12. antibodies destroy/render harmless/inactivate antigens/viruses/bacteria/pathogens

Coherence

- Divided into clear sections
- At least 3 points on viruses
- And at least 2 points on lymphocytes
- *Total of five points required*

Reference

- No mention of details of replication/protein synthesis/ phagocytes
- At least 3 points on viruses
- And at least 2 points on lymphocytes
- *Total of five points required*

Hey! I've done it

iBrightRED
PUBLISHING

Published by Bright Red Publishing Ltd, 6 Stafford Street, Edinburgh, EH3 7AU
Tel: 0131 220 5804, Fax: 0131 220 6710, enquiries: sales@brightredpublishing.co.uk,
www.brightredpublishing.co.uk

Official SQA answers to 978-1-84948-209-7
2007-2011